THE ISSUES COLLECTION

COLLECTION EDITOR:
GILLDA LEITENBERG

Futures

EDITED BY JOHN H. ALTHOUSE

♦ ♦ ♦

To Mary and Carl, my parents,
who guided my first feeble steps into the future
and to all my students, past and present,
who are the future

McGraw-Hill Ryerson Limited

Toronto • Montreal • New York • Auckland • Bogotá
Caracas • Lisbon • London • Madrid • Mexico • Milan
New Delhi • Paris • San Juan • Singapore • Sydney • Tokyo

Futures
The Issues Collection

Copyright © McGraw-Hill Ryerson Limited, 1994
All rights reserved. No part of this publication may be reproduced or transmitted in any form or by any means, or stored in a data base or retrieval system, without the prior written permission of McGraw-Hill Ryerson Limited.

ISBN 0-07-551523-7

1 2 3 4 5 6 7 8 9 10 BG 3 2 1 0 9 8 7 6 5 4

Printed and bound in Canada

Canadian Cataloguing in Publication Data

Main entry under title:

Futures

(The issues collection)
ISBN 0-07-551523-7

1. Readers (Elementary) 2. Readers (Secondary).
3. Readers — Maturation (Psychology). 4. Readers —
Forecasting. 5. Maturation (Psychology) — Literary
collections. 6. Forecasting — Literary collections.
I. Althouse, John H. II. Series.

PE1121.F8 1993   808'.0427   C93-095195-6

Editor: *Kathy Evans*
Senior Supervising Editor: *Carol Altilia*
Permissions Editor: *Jacqueline Donovan*
Designer: *Mary Opper*
Typesetter: *Pages Design Ltd.*
Photo Researcher: *Elaine Freedman*
Cover Illustrator: *Nick Vitacco*

This book was manufactured in Canada using acid-free and recycled paper.

Contents

Introduction

"There is always one moment in childhood when the door opens and lets the future in." — Graham Greene

The purpose of this volume of The Issues Collection — Futures — *is to provide you with open doors through which you can take a look at your future. The future that I mean is not the one that has formed in the minds of science fiction writers. It is, rather, the individual and personal future that awaits each one of us. This book is to be a guide to considering your personal future.*

You will need skills to face your future: you will be required to grow, make decisions, and deal with change. You will assume new and exciting roles. You are dealing with becoming more independent, with making your own decisions. You might someday have to consider the roles of worker, spouse, parent — and all that those roles imply. Your skill in preparing for and dealing with these changes will help shape your future life.

The world of the future might be radically different from the one we know now because of the rapid growth of technology. Some of the selections in this book explore this theme. But too many people try to sum up the future with the word technology. While the importance of technological growth on our future can't be denied, this book also recognizes that human values and relationships will play a large part in the direction of our future world.

It's a puzzle, the future. But I hope that this book will offer you a few of those moments in which the future is let in, and that you take a peek at it to find a meaningful and hopeful place for yourself there.

John H. Althouse

Metaphors
of the
Future

◆◆◆

The future is like a large fun park filled with roller coasters. You can visit them all and use your admission price to the fullest or you can be frightened and waste it. You can watch other people go on a roller coaster and then try it out yourself. You may dislike one and then turn out to like it but once you are going forward you can't change your mind and go back again.

Benjamin Vlietstra
Grade 8 (1990)

Life is a road filled with its many ups and downs and turn offs along the way which you may or may not want to take. There is always a destination but you do not always know what that destination is going to be. The very health and life of the road depend on the owner.

Peter Holloway
Grade 8 (1990)

The future is like climbing a tree; the higher you climb, the more branches you discover. You can never quite see the top until you get there, but if that's all you concentrate on, your chances of falling increase.

Christie Pentland
Grade 8 (1989)

The future is like a live volcano. Not knowing when it will erupt is very unsettling. When it does erupt the lava can flow away leaving the humans to peacefully enjoy their lives, or it can burn what is in its path leaving everything behind lifeless.

Steve Williams
Grade 7 (1991)

Life is like a piano. You keep looking for the right notes until you can play a song. But remember, every song must have an ending.

Erica Domsey
Grade 7 (1989)

The future is a pair of scissors cutting out a snow-flake. You can control where you want to go but if you move the scissors in the wrong direction, anything could happen. You might find that the snowflake has fallen apart and you have to start over again but it could also happen that the wrong cut could have turned out for the better and the snowflake came out looking even more beautiful. Thinking ahead could save time and prevent you from making the wrong moves. The future is a pair of scissors and only you can guide them along.

Cathy Chan
Grade 8 (1990)

Jason, Becoming

♦ ♦ ♦

BY

GAIL

FOX

There is no room
that does not bear
your touch, your innocent
destruction, all things
become toys, vehicles of pleasure,
to pull, to push, to tear, to break,
there is no limit.

Once all this was confined
to your playpen, then your maturing
limbs broke out, arranged
the house in your own way,
heedless of our objections, our
reprimands, our endless corrections.

Some day, child, we will
claim the house back, and
you will let it go,
worlds facing you, proud,
excited in your young becoming.

For My Children

♦♦♦

BY

ROBIN

MATHEWS

Out of the clamour of cries
calling and calling
you decide,
because growing means deciding,
means moving in the mind;
it means making up your mind.

They want you.
They want you convinced
that to grow is to live *better than,*
is to live in a ruling class —
that you grow by making your way there,
growing.

I pray for you.
I pray for your strength
for your indignation —
not to surrender in the face of all odds —
I pray for the love in you to grow into fearless certainty
beyond my certainty
that only by changing what growing means
here
can you call yourself
or anybody
growing
free.

Hopes and Expectations:

How Teenagers View the Future

♦♦♦

BY

REGINALD W. BIBBY
AND DONALD C. POSTERSKI

Teenagers today are scared. With unemployment, the economy, divorce and the world's peace situation — we all wonder what will happen.
— a sixteen-year-old female from rural Quebec

Living the teenage years in our society is like driving in heavy traffic without knowing where you want to go or whether you will be able to get there. In addition to many quandaries about themselves, teenagers are increasingly feeling puzzled about a world that is extremely complex. They are bombarded with expectations from parents, teachers, ministers, advertisers, the media, and their friends. As they stand in the midst of the traffic, they are forced not only to dream but to plan. With plans come hopes, and with hopes, expectations.

The Canadian Dream
While often overshadowed by the American dream of progressing from "log cabin to White House," there is also a pervasive Canadian Dream. It is learned in childhood and is the product of our central institutions: the school, the media, the family, the church, the government and, of

course, the business community. Teenagers have taken in with mother's milk the views: "This is a land of opportunity. Education will open doors for you. Individual excellence will be rewarded. Work hard and you will be successful. The best, after all, eventually arrive at the top, and enjoy the good life."

Lands of opportunity make promises and breed optimism. Some 70% of teenagers agree with the ideal that "anyone who works hard will rise to the top." One grade twelve female from a small southern Ontario town proclaims:

> At our age we can do anything and be whoever we want to be if we want it bad enough.

Interestingly, many adults who have had to wrestle with the ideal have modified their expectations. Only 44% of them still concur with such an idea. Their disillusionment is readily apparent.

One message society transmits to young people is that the good life requires an education. When asked "What do you plan to do after high school?" about 75% indicated that they want to go on for further education (see Table 1).

Although less than 20% of the parents of the teenagers surveyed have university degrees themselves, the big teen dream is to go to university. When teenagers are fifteen years old, almost 65% of them plan to experience life on campus (see Table 1). However, by the time those same teenagers are nineteen, less than 40% still see themselves as university-bound. Over a period of four years, the dream of a university education dissolves for more than half of Canadian teenagers. By the time registration lines form on campus, the numbers have been cut in half again. Only about 15% of all high-school students — under 1 in 7 — actually attend university following graduation from high school. Most teenagers taste the pain of relinquishing their university education dream before they turn twenty.

As the number of young people intending to go to university declines, the number planning to try to get a job increases. At least two factors seem to be involved. Contrary to societal propaganda and parental hopes, a university education is still beyond the financial means of many. Further, given the state of the economy, university degrees are seen as having dubious value if the primary objective is to qualify for a job....

Regional variations in post-high-school plans are minor. Teenagers in Ontario and the Atlantic region are slightly more likely than others to look to university rather than technical or business post-secondary institutions.

Perhaps reflecting the fact that females now believe that a wide range of occupations is available to them, a slightly higher proportion of young women than young men indicate that they plan to go to university; relatedly, males are somewhat more apt to see their post-high-school lives involving a job or a technical or business-school training (see Table 1).

TABLE 1	Plans After High School by Region, Gender, and Age (in percentages)					

"What do you plan to do after high school?"

	Try to Get a Job	Go to Univ.	Go to Tech-Bus.	Other	Un-decided	Totals
Nationally	16	54	23	3	4	100
British Columbia	16	47	28	3	6	100
Prairies	18	48	24	5	5	100
Ontario	15	61	17	3	4	100
Quebec	15	50	28	3	4	100
Atlantic	15	58	19	5	3	100
Males	17	51	25	4	3	100
Females	14	57	21	3	5	100
15	10	63	22	2	3	100
16	13	53	25	4	5	100
17	17	53	21	5	4	100
18	23	51	20	2	4	100
19	33	37	21	1	8	100

Life Beyond School

The question of what young people will do after they finish their education has been cited as their most pressing personal concern. Only 1 in 10 teenagers say they are not troubled significantly by the issue. This concern among teenagers is pervasive in all regions of Canada at all ages and characterizes males and females equally. The paramount question for teenagers is the "life-after question," not with respect to death but to school.

As a means of probing teenagers' plans beyond the classroom, we asked:

When you finish your education do you plan to:
1. Get a job, and eventually marry
2. Get a job, but not marry
3. Get married, and not work outside the home
4. Get married, but also work outside the home

While options 1 and 4 appear to be quite similar, they were carefully designed to explore the respondents' emphasis. For those teenagers planning to combine the roles, option 1 is weighted towards one's career, while the fourth choice emphasizes the marriage side.

About 7 in 10 say they intend to get a job and eventually marry, while only 1 in 10 emphasize getting married but also working outside the home (see Table 2). Most of the remainder indicate they plan to get a job but not marry. And only 1% say that they plan to get married and not work outside the home.

An analysis by region reveals considerable consistency throughout the country, with the exception of Quebec. One in 4 teenagers in that province indicate that they intend to work but stay single, compared with only 10% in other regions.

Perhaps somewhat surprisingly, only 1% of female teenagers say they intend to marry and not work outside the home. If translated into behaviour, such plans would represent a major change from the current situation. Currently only about 50% of all women work for pay, with 60% of these women married, 30% single, and 10% widowed, separated, or divorced. Among them are 58% of the mothers of the teenagers in our survey. Regardless of the values one places on such possible imminent change, the implications for the size of the work force and the problem of unemployment are somewhat staggering.

It is also interesting to recall a relevant finding from another part of this study, that 17% of teens feel that "married women should not work if their husbands are capable of supporting them." About 20% of males are in agreement with this position, compared with only 5% of females. And the young women who plan to work are adamant. Some 95% of the females who envision having a career without marriage disagree with such traditionalism, as do 95% of the females who, personally, plan to marry. Something, it would appear, is going to have to give...

"When you finish your education, do you plan to:"

	Get a Job, Eventually Marry	Get a Job, Not Marry	Marry, Not Work Outside of Home	Marry, Work Outside of Home	Total
Nationally	72	15	1	12	100
British Columbia	77	10	0	13	100
Prairies	78	10	1	11	100
Ontario	75	11	1	13	100
Quebec	62	26	2	10	100
Atlantic	77	11	1	11	100
Males	77	16	1	6	100
Females	68	14	1	17	100

Employment

Until recent years, there was a Canadian assumption that jobs are available to those who want to work. The availability of employment was almost treated as a basic "human right." Recent recession, technological advances, a work force that includes more women, and the inability of governments individually and collectively to control the economy have all forced us to surrender this assumption.

Canadian young people have witnessed the impact of declining school enrolments in their everyday lives. They read in the newspaper that school boards are being forced to release an annual quota of teachers. They say goodbye to teachers who will not be returning in the fall. They sense the trauma in others, and feel the loss themselves. They notice that the average age of high-school teachers is increasing.

Young people are worried. Society's economic promises are in danger of being unfulfilled. Little wonder that, in needing some institutional source to blame, teenagers are critical of government. Aware of the plight of many about to graduate and seeing the employment problem ahead for himself, an Alberta sixteen-year-old laments:

> [Teenagers] go to school for twelve years and when they get out of school they have to fight for work, and if they don't get work they get labelled as young punks or lazy bums. It isn't their fault

they can't find work. The government isn't helping them any.

Increasing economic and social strain seems inevitable. And this strain will only be intensified by present high expectations. On the one hand, teenagers recognize the potential employment problem. They acknowledge with one sixteen-year-old from the Okanagan that:

> with or without education, jobs are scarce because of the economy.

On the other hand, while they perceive unemployment as a severe problem, they continue to have a remarkable amount of optimism about their *own personal* employment prospects. More than 70% maintain that when they complete their education, they "think that [they] will be able to find a good job." Optimism about future employment varies only slightly by region. These variations reflect actual employment conditions in being somewhat higher in Ontario, Quebec, and the Prairies, and slightly lower in B.C. and the Atlantic regions. There is little difference in employment optimism by either age or, significantly, *gender.* Female teenagers have as high employment hopes as males. Only a minority share the realism expressed by a Charlottetown grade eleven female:

> I might have the job requirements but the jobs might not be there.

Even fewer admit to the extreme pessimism of a Newfoundland grade ten student:

> There won't be any jobs around. If older people who are more qualified can't find jobs, how can I?

Marriage

There has been considerable speculation in recent decades about the future of conventional marriage. A recent survey by Family Services of America has projected that by the year 2000 there will be a drop in the percentage of North Americans who marry — to 85% from 90%. The Family Services report attributes such a decline to "weakening religious, social and legal taboos, greater sexual freedom promoting continued growth of cohabitation, single-person households, unwed single-parent families, and homosexual couples."

Our survey findings, however, do not point to such a decline. While at this point in time 85% of teenagers say they plan to marry, it seems sound to assert that this is a minimum figure. Many will undoubtedly marry who, in their late teens, are not envisioning doing so. Whatever they are observing about the present state of marriage and divorce in our society, most teenagers still believe that their desire to be loved can best be fulfilled in a marital relationship. We are not alone in our assertion. American family researchers Flake-Hobson, Robinson, and Skeen write, "Adolescents do not agree with the idea that 'marriage is out of date' and most eventually plan to marry and have children."

Their comment about children holds for Canada. More than 50% of the teenagers in our sample indicate that they would like to have two children, while 20% envision having three. About 15% would like four or more children, while the remainder want either only one child (7%) or none at all (8%).

A highly significant pattern that thus emerges concerning "life beyond school" is the similarity of expectations for females and males. The national survey reveals that Canadian teenage females presently differ very little from their male counterparts in planning to attend university and have a career, while also marrying and having children. This would seem to represent a very important change from past gender expectations. Accordingly, it is now precarious to assert, as did status of women advisory council representatives meeting in Quebec in late 1984, that the "women's movement has had little impact on adolescent girls who believe love and marriage are more important than education and a good job." Reality not withstanding, males and females share very similar expectations.

The Survivor Generation

Canada
Worried, they yearn for work

♦ ♦ ♦

BY

JEAN KAVANAGH

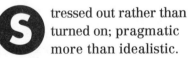

S tressed out rather than turned on; pragmatic more than idealistic.

The keywords for Canada's youth have changed over the decades.

"They all want to be rich," said Colleen Garrard, head of counselling at Vancouver's Templeton secondary school.

"Money comes up right away when I ask them about a job. Only some of the more perceptive kids talk about getting a job they'll like."

A tight, demanding job market and a drop in the number of good-paying jobs for the untrained have boosted competition for university places, putting stress on high school students.

"Some of my friends have cried in class," said Tazim Somani, 18, of Vancouver's Magee secondary school. "There's so much pressure and they are scared because we know there are no jobs for those not qualified and competition is high."

About 18 per cent of the 18-to-24 age group in Canada goes to university, and awareness of the slow economy has brought out a pragmatism in many.

Susan Clark, who just graduated from a suburban Toronto high school, says many of her classmates are struggling for university entrance because they think it's the only option for a secure future.

"There's a general feeling you have to get a university degree now and that we'll have to work a lot harder than our parents did to achieve the same.

"You can't just go to a corporation and get a job anymore."

Ronald Hinch, a sociologist at the University of Guelph in Ontario said today's young people have learned to put themselves first.

"We're entering a very individualistic age, much more individualistic than the Me Generation," he said. "We taught them that — to put No. 1 ahead of all the others."

The increasing desire to go to university and the competition once there is pushing many young people to their emotional brink, said sociologist Alan King.

And while Canadians aged 11 to 15 are healthier and more athletic than their counterparts in 10 European countries, psychologically they fall short, said King, who recently completed a study for Health and Welfare Canada. Depression, loneliness and strained relationships with parents were more evident with the 5000 Canadians surveyed than with the Europeans, King said. The diminished job market is turning average students who don't make the university grade into "losers in a competitive society."

Students who do make it into university face age-old academic pressures, but many have the added burden of holding a job at the same time.

Jocelyn Charren of the Canadian Federation of Students says young people may participate less in politics "because most students work, and work longer hours than they used to."

But politics remains a passion for many. Jeff Gibbs, 24, of Vancouver, was spurred to environmental action after a trip to the rain forests of Brazil and Borneo, and he later transformed the experience into building the Environmental Youth Alliance, a national action group.

"Youths are talking about a lot of issues — AIDS, sex, jobs — but there is a general concern about the environment," said Gibbs.

The environment is a fad for many young people but others want to become active, he believes. The traditional political system, however, leaves them out.

"A lot of students hang out in arcades who wouldn't do that if they could focus their energy on something positive," said Gibbs.

He said traditional political parties are "going nowhere with youths," a view shared by some of his counterparts in Britain who also feel the political establishment leaves out the concerns of the young.

But youth can be a political force.

Those aged 15 to 24 represent 14 per cent of the Canadian population.

Mario Dumoint, a 22-year-old economics student who heads the powerful youth wing of Quebec's Liberal party, believes Quebec youth are politically ahead of their counterparts elsewhere in Canada.

"We have a voice. We have proof of that," he said, referring to the youth wing's 30-per cent-control of voting delegates at all party conventions.

Sociologist Raymond Hudon of Laval University agrees, noting that more young Quebecers are working with, instead of against, the system.

"In the 1970s, the mobilization of young people was greater in Quebec than in the rest of Canada," said Hudon.

"There was the nationalist movement, the referendum on independence and student unions were very strong."

United States
Forgotten, they lose
their faith

◆◆◆

B Y

CALVIL WOODWARD

American youth of today are growing up without applause.

They've been judged as a "rising tide of mediocrity," lacking "core moral values," suffering from "herky-jerky brain" and needing nothing so much as a "good, swift kick in the pants."

Various studies have gone on to say they are financially illiterate, uninformed and uninvolved in national and world issues, and so sedentary their "cardiovascular trend is ominous."

Yet they act "as if the whole world owes them, as if they have a right to win," as one think-tank put it.

Perhaps not since the so-called Lost Generation of the 1920s has American youth had such a rough ride from well-meaning, if pompous elders.

"Two decades ago, older generations saw great promise in youth. Not now — not these youths anyway." So say William Strauss and Neil Howe, authors of *Generations,* a book that explores the generational cycles of American history.

"No other generation in living memory has come of age with such a sense of social distance — of adults doing so little for them and expecting so little of them."

Yet after cataloguing damning insults against youth from almost every corner of society, Strauss and Howe are cautiously optimistic.

They see in youth today a sharp-eyed pragmatism, a bag of savvy tricks and an instinct for survival that just might carry them through.

"More than anyone, they have developed a seasoned talent for getting the most out of a bad hand."

"Today's American youth are more apt to come from a household where both parents work. More homes are racked by family separation — U.S. divorce rates in the 1980s doubled from the 1960s and tripled from the 1950s.

They go to high schools that are widely considered second-rate, then hang out at the mall. A decade-long fitness study found their bodies flabby.

Overall, the diminished sense of promise at large seems to have particularly infected the young, a group whose politics, fashions, musical tastes and general attitudes have for decades had an influence far beyond the country's borders.

Like their parents, many youth have lost faith in leaders and institutions. But they haven't nominated their own.

"I don't see a real drive for this generation," says Claire Loebs of Pocatello, Idaho, an 18-year-old college sophomore who feels caught between the 1980s gold-rush mentality and the idealism of youth 20 years ago.

"The overall impression is, the country isn't doing anything, just kind of stagnating."

Maybe it's just the long, tough haul out of recession, or something deeper, but the United States as the land of opportunity doesn't seem to ring true at the moment.

In a gritty west Philadelphia neighborhood, where Falakah Fattah has spent 25 years "adopting" gang members and turning street talents into job skills, upward mobility seems harder than ever. "You can't take a kid who controlled 500 other kids and tell him to work at McDonald's," she says, tracing a route often taken in the inner city for lack of anything better. "All that leadership ability lost on hamburgers!"

Today's adults, many of whom had good times in the pre-AIDS sexual revolution, despair over the inability of teens to resist temptations of the flesh — although youth endorse chastity as an ideal more than their parents did.

Drug use is increasingly frowned on by the young, except for alcohol. Religion has made a comeback.

American teens may not be able to find Canada on a map, but they are more inclined than their parents were to volunteer in the local community.

And despite the widely criticized public schools, a greater percentage of Americans than Canadians go to university.

On campus, even high achievers like Michael Musante fret about the future. At 19, the native of Follansbee, W. Va., is the student president at George

Washington. Once, Musante said, "you could graduate from high school, get a job working in the steel mill and...retire and live off a very nice pension and have enough money to send your child to college.

"That's not going to happen. That's gone. Those are things my generation has to adapt to."

Authors Howe and Strauss don't believe the ingredients are in place for "13ers" — as they call the 13th generation since the U.S. War of Independence — to rally behind a common cause. "Far more than older generations, 13ers come with myriads of regional subgroups and ethnic minicultures, each thinking its own thoughts, listening to its own music, laying its own plans, and paying little heed to each other."

In the end, they may not be unlike the Lost Generation, author Gertrude Stein's description of a brainy, creative and jaundiced bunch whose manners and morals were judged by elders as the country's likely ruination.

Britain
Tougher, they live
for today

◆◆◆

BY STEPHEN WARD

John Ranger peers through his cab window, a fresh face on a street banked by grim office towers and populated by business suits.

"Piccadilly Circus it is," Ranger chirps with a strong north England accent. He turns up his radio for a full blast of hard rock.

Three years ago, at 16, Ranger left school, fed up with teachers, books and tests. He wanted a job.

Driving a cab in London provided steady work and immediate rewards.

"The way I see it," Ranger says as his black cab hurtles down a narrow lane, "if you're stuck in a recession, you gotta survive.

"Don't go chasing some iffy dream. Driving gets me a job, money, a flat. I got me pub mates. I mean, what do you want?"

It's a view that would have put Ranger at odds with a lot of young people in the 1960s, when teenagers were in the vanguard of a youth culture that marched against war and helped turn the world on to everything from the Beatles to miniskirts.

Young Brits today seem more conservative and lack the influence or cohesiveness of the '60s baby boomers, who — now in their 40s — have become part of the establishment.

John Bynner, head of the Social Statistics Unit of London's City University, recently completed a study that reached some worrisome conclusions: many young people in Britain prefer to take almost any type of a job rather than job training, and half of them leave school by 16.

They're apathetic towards politics, although some issues, such as equal opportunity and the environment, spark interest.

"They're not Maggie Thatcher's children, despite growing up under the prime minister," Bynner said. "Few want to pay more taxes but they want to receive more government benefits."

Margaret Rice is among the 15 per cent of British youth who go on to university. An undergraduate student at Oxford University, Rice, 20, hopes to obtain a master's degree in history.

To her, a university education provides access to the good life and scaling of class barriers. It doesn't mean she's apathetic about her society.

"The general election (April 1992) completely ignored the sort of issues that interest young people — like education, equality of the sexes and environment," Rice said.

"So we say to the political parties, a plague on all your houses. But given a proper chance, we'd tackle the problems and offer answers."

The Girl Who Couldn't See Herself

♦♦♦

BY LEENA DHINGRA

nce upon a time there was a girl who couldn't see herself very clearly, and so she kept stumbling and losing herself all the time. For, since she couldn't see herself, she didn't know what she was, or where she fitted in, or how she should behave.

She decided to do something about it and went and bought herself a large mirror and put it up in her room. But when she looked at herself in it, all she saw was a blur. This was most confusing. She turned away from the mirror and sat down to think about it, and then, through the corner of her eye, she caught a reflection of herself in the mirror, but when she turned to see what it was, all that faced her was the same blur. This confused her even more.

She put on her coat, went out and walked down the street, but nobody seemed to notice her. Even in the shop, the cashier simply looked at the goods in the basket, took the note and placed the change on the counter. The girl started to wonder if, maybe, she was invisible, and so, on her way home, she walked right in the middle of the pavement to see what would happen. People gave way to her, some even grumbled as they almost bumped into her, but she returned home feeling reassured that, at least, she wasn't invisible.

"Really, this is most strange," she thought. "Why is it that others can see me and I can't see myself?" Then she had an idea. "Of course," she said to herself. "What I'll do is to ask someone to tell me who and what I am, and then I'll know..."

"You are a round soft ball," said the first person she asked. "And what you should do is bounce and simply roll along." So off went the girl, bouncing away and rolling along until she landed — ploof — into the gutter. She managed to crawl out and dragged herself home.

"No, no, no, no, no!" said the next person. "You are a square box. Firm and hard with sharp corners. You stand square and straight like other boxes." So, trying to make herself as boxish as she could, she went off to join the other square boxes. She tried to smile and stand as firmly and squarely as she could, but she was so dented and bruised that she didn't even appear like a straight, firm square box any more.

The next person told her that she was quite definitely a triangle! There was no doubt about it and she should just balance herself on her tip like a spinning-top. She tried that, and it felt lovely. So she spun away round and round and round until she got so dizzy that she lost herself completely. She returned home, feeling sad and lonely. She looked at the blur in the mirror, and no longer knew what to do.

Outside the sun was shining and she decided to go for a walk in the park. "If I were a tree, I could just grow. If I were a sun, I could simply shine. If I were a bench, I could just wait. But since I don't know what I am, how can I know what I'm supposed to do? With these thoughts she sat down wearily on the bench and looked around her at people spinning, standing square, bouncing, jumping and flying about. She felt so sorry for herself that she started to cry, and didn't notice that someone else had come to sit on the same bench.

"Isn't it a beautiful day!" said the someone. She stopped crying and turned to find a woman sitting beside her. She had a quiet face and smiled a wonderful smile. She smiled back at her, and her own smile warmed her heart and felt so right. The sun shone, the wind blew gently, fluttering the leaves on the tree, and the bench felt still and comforting. Her smile grew.

"You have a beautiful smile!" said the woman.

"Thank you," replied the girl.

The woman laughed. "Why do you thank me?" she said. "You should thank yourself. Thank the sun, thank the tree, thank life..." She continued looking around her.

She suddenly felt very happy and joined the laughter. "Okay, then, I'll thank them all and thank you, too."

"All right," said the woman. "If you thank them all, then you may thank me, too."

They sat for a while in a comfortable silence, and then the woman got up to go. As she was leaving she said to the girl, "Treasure your smile... and be happy" and she walked away with a light step. The girl stayed on the silent bench, glowing in the warmth of the woman's smile. She looked around her and it seemed as though everything smiled; the sun, the tree, the people, even the wind.

She walked home feeling light. In her room she turned to the mirror and saw the same blur — but also a smile...

"What a beautiful smile," she said out loud, and then, as she looked at the smile, a light outline started to emerge around the blur...

Telephone Romance

◆◆◆

BY

CATHY

BEVERIDGE

Mike, phone," screamed Gerry from the study. "It's your tele-phone girlfriend."

I wrenched the phone out of my little brother's hands, smiling inwardly at his oddly appropriate description of Jennifer. "Hello."

"Don't you just hate it when they do that?" Jennifer's voice asked.

I smiled into the receiver. "Yes, except it doesn't happen much around here. I don't get many phone calls from girls."

"Sure, sure," she teased. "Well, I hope you don't mind me calling, but I just found out the most incredible news."

"Which is?" I prompted.

"Our schools are in a basketball tournament at St. Francis High School this weekend."

Both of us were avid basketball players and fans, except she cheered for the Lakers and I liked the Celtics. "The same tournament?"

"Yep." It starts tomorrow and runs until Sunday. Just thought you might want to come watch us beat your team."

"Not a chance of you guys doing that," I said, dismissing her remark, my mind racing. It was the first mention either of us had made about getting together in person since that day three weeks ago when she'd dialed the wrong number while trying to find her little brother. She'd sounded so certain she knew me, that she'd even had me wondering if I didn't know her. By the time I'd discovered that I really didn't, I'd decided that I should and had managed to wrangle her number out of her. After the initial embarrassment, Jennifer had seen the humour in the situation. Now I was finally going to get a chance to meet her.

"You, beat us? We haven't lost a game all season," she reminded me.

"But you haven't played St. Vincent because we're not in your division."

"Well, why don't you come watch on the weekend and we'll see."

I did not respond immediately. Half of me ached to meet this girl while the other half warned me that things would only come to an end if I did.

"I, uh, I can't make it tomorrow night. My folks are going out and I have to watch my little brother." That much was true.

"Well, maybe Saturday then?" Jennifer asked hopefully. "In fact, if we win Friday, and St. Vincent's girls' team wins, we play each other Saturday morning at ten."

"Now that would be the game to watch," I agreed.

Jennifer sounded hopeful. "So we'll see you Saturday then?" She paused, then asked awkwardly, "How will I know you?"

"I'll wear my Celtics jersey. You won't be able to miss me." I laughed, trying to hide my nervousness.

"I'll watch for you." There was another strained pause. "Remember, I'm number twenty-two, she said."

"I will. Well, good luck tomorrow."

"Thanks. See you on the weekend."

I hung the receiver up softly. In just two days I'd have the answers to all my questions. In just two days I'd know if she were blond, had green eyes, or were taller than me. I doodled on the message pad on the desk. And in just two days, she'd know I had two artificial legs.

"Are you done yet?" Gerry inquired, sticking his head into the study. "I have to call Danny."

I nodded and stood up, my knees clicking and grinding noisily.

"Yee," Gerry grimaced. "Those sound awful. Need a new pair?"

"Maybe I should call Dr. Seagram and arrange for another fitting," Mom suggested from the hall, her voice half-lost in the linen closet.

I shook my head. "Naw, they're just a little stiff, that's all."

I brushed past Mom on the way to my room. It was amazing how people adapted to things. Fifteen months ago, right after the boating accident, we'd all gone around trying to pretend nothing had changed. Now we were discussing a new set of legs as if they were a new pair of shoes. I grinned despite myself. It hadn't been easy at first — it still wasn't, but I was learning to fill in the gaps. I glanced up at the trophy on my bureau. Wheelchair basketball certainly helped. And so did Jennifer, even though I'd never met her. Girls like her didn't seem to wander in my direction very often. I grimaced. Then again, two artificial legs certainly didn't help. It wasn't something most girls put down on their list of most desirable qualities.

Not everyone had adapted to the new me. I could still remember the expression on Tara's face when she'd called it all off after the accident. She'd said that it had nothing to do with my loss, but who wanted a boyfriend without legs? I plunked down on my bed. I could always go to the tournament and not say anything. But then what? If our relationship did go on, she'd have to know eventually. And it would be easier if she called it off now rather than later. I pummelled my pillow and reconsidered my dilemma.

By Friday night, my curiosity had won me over. On Saturday morning I would go and say nothing.

The game was already underway when I arrived at St. Francis, and Jennifer's team had a commanding lead. It took only a second to spot her. She was approximately my height and her long, black hair was pulled back in a braid. Dark, curled bangs framed her face and her eyes were intense. Not only that, she was a terrific basketball player. I followed her progress up and down the court, taking in the real image of this girl whose voice I knew so well. She was not what I had expected, but then I wasn't sure exactly what I *had* expected. I glanced down at my Celtics jersey, half-hidden underneath my jacket. There were only a few minutes left in the game. If I took my coat off now, she would spot me as soon as the game ended. I unzipped my jacket and hesitated. Was I what she had imagined? My knees throbbed. With Jennifer at the foul line, I left the gymnasium and pushed my way to a pay phone.

"Hello Mrs. Symko. This is Mike calling. I was wondering if I could leave a message for Jennifer." I chewed on my bottom lip, feeling my heart sink. "I was going to try to get over to the basketball tournament today, but my family's decided to go out of town at the last minute. Tell her I'll call her Sunday night when we get back."

I could still hear the pounding of basketballs and cheering crowd as I made my way out the school door.

At nine o'clock Sunday, I was still pacing around the study trying to decide what to do. At the very least I owed Jennifer a phone call. That was the easy part. I'd just say that my folks had decided to visit my grandmother in Red Deer for the weekend and I hadn't been able to make it to the game. The tough part was going to be the next time Jennifer wanted to get together. Why couldn't she just be happy with a telephone boyfriend — one that sounded completely normal, one that sounded like he had two real legs? I sank into the chair just as the phone rang. "I'll get it," I hollered and picked up the receiver.

Her voice was thick and bright, like sunshine through a screen, and I felt a sudden wave of despair sweep over me.

"Hi, did you just get home?" she asked.

"Uh, yeah," I answered gruffly. "Sorry about the sudden change of plans. My dad doesn't always consult us on these matters."

"I know that feeling," replied Jennifer. "You missed a good tournament, though."

I couldn't help but catch her enthusiasm. "Really? How did you do?"

"We lost to the Barons in overtime during the final. Can you believe it?"

"Tough luck. How did you play?"

"Great, actually. In the semi-finals, I shot a twenty-five-point game."

"Wow! Remind me not to play against you." I was impressed. I sighed sadly.

"What's wrong, Mike?"

There was a tenderness in her voice that I'd never noticed before. How could I explain to her that I was wrong. I swallowed the lump in my throat. "Nothing, why?" I asked, trying to sound upbeat.

"You just don't seem like your usual self, that's all." She paused. "Did something happen on the weekend?"

For a split second I debated telling her the truth. Maybe, just maybe, she'd understand. I glanced down at my knees and winced. "I, I'm just a little tired, I guess." I yawned to emphasize the fact.

"Well, I had better let you get some sleep," Jennifer said weakly. "I'll talk to you soon?"

"I'll phone you tomorrow night," I assured her. "'Bye." I let the receiver fall. "Damn!"

By morning, I had made a decision. Immediately after supper, I locked myself in the study and phoned Jennifer. I had only a few minutes before my basketball game, but it wouldn't take long anyway.

"Hi, Jennifer," I said nervously. "Listen, I've got a game tonight, so I just have a second, but, uh, I was wondering if you'd be able to, uh, go to the Calgary Eight-Eights game at the Corral this Friday? I'm sure Dad would pick us up and drive you home if you could get down there. Maybe we could meet somewhere and take the transit." There, I'd done it.

"I'd love to," Jennifer said. "What time does the game start?"

"Seven o'clock. There's an ice-cream shop in the bottom of my dad's office building downtown. How about if we meet there first?"

"Sure. Will you be wearing your Celtics jersey?"

"I will," I grinned, remembering that she still had no idea what I looked like. Hurriedly, I gave her directions and zipped out the door to the van where Dad was waiting. Now if I could just get Dad to cooperate!

About halfway there, I broached the subject. "Dad, do you think you could take my wheelchair to work with you on Friday?"

He stared at me, his eyebrows knit together in bewilderment. "Why would I do that?"

"Because I'd like to take this girl to the basketball game and..." I launched into my explanation.

"I see," Dad murmured when I had finished. "And you don't want to wear your legs because..."

"I want her to know right away. I don't want to have to tell her."

Dad licked his bottom lip thoughtfully. "You know Mike, maybe you're not giving this girl enough credit. Why don't you just tell her before you go?"

"No!" I said defiantly. "Don't you remember what happened with Tara?" I burrowed down into the seat. "Now will you take my wheelchair or not?"

"Okay," Dad agreed. "I'll put it in the van Thursday night."

I met Dad in his office after school on Friday. He was meeting some clients after work so he showed me where the van was parked and wished me luck. Down in the parking lot, I lifted the chair out, snapped my legs off and deposited them in the van. Then I wheeled my way up the ramp and into the ice-cream shop. I was half an hour early. The waitress offered to seat me at an empty table in the corner, but I told her I'd wait until the table directly in front of the door became available. Eventually my table cleared and I wheeled over to it. Then I took off my coat and made sure that I was sitting facing the mirror behind the counter with my back in full view of the door, wheelchair obviously visible. With ten minutes to spare, I ordered a milkshake and tried to calm my nerves. I slurped the shake and waited.

On my last slurp, I saw her walking up the street, trying to read the sign above us. She looked terrific, her long, black hair streaming down her back. I tried to look away, but couldn't. She spotted the Celtics jersey right away and smiled. I braced myself for her next reaction, the one to come when she saw the wheelchair. But the smile never altered. She brushed a strand of hair away from her face and glided towards the table.

"Mike?" she said, leaning forward so I could see her.

"Jennifer," I said nervously, lifting my head and looking into her eyes. "Sit down, please." I pushed my chair back and indicated the seat across from me. She had to have seen the wheelchair by now.

She sat down opposite me in the sunshine. "I can't believe that I'm finally getting a chance to meet you," she grinned. "After talking to a voice for so long, you start to wonder what the person it belongs to looks like."

"So am I what you imagined?" I asked, giving her the chance to get it all over with.

She leaned back from the table and scrutinized me. "Actually, I thought you'd be blond," she observed. Her eyes swept down my body to the floor. "And I thought you would have worn your legs tonight."

I knocked my empty glass over. "What, how...when did you find out about my legs?"

She smirked and her eyes twinkled mischievously. "Oh, about a week after I first called you up with that wrong number."

I stared incredulously at her.

"Do you know a guy named Frank Hunley?" she asked.

I nodded. "Frank's in my homeroom at school."

"Well, he's my cousin. After I found out what school you went to, I was dying of curiosity so I asked Frank about you. He told me then." She looked fondly at me.

"You mean, you've known all this time?" She nodded. "Why didn't you say something?"

"I was waiting for you to tell me. Besides, what difference does it make anyway?"

I wanted to leap across the table and hug her right then, but I didn't want to make a scene. Besides, I couldn't have leaped even if I'd wanted to. My legs were still in the van.

"Listen," I said awkwardly, "why don't you order a milkshake or something while I zip out to the van and get my legs." I glanced up sheepishly at her. "They're a little more convenient."

"You mean, they're here and you didn't wear them? Why wouldn't you...?" She stopped, suddenly understanding why I had chosen not to wear them. "Mike, you didn't really think that..." I blushed a deep shade of red and she laughed.

"Well, if you promise to come back, I think I'll have a root beer float."

I wheeled quickly out of the restaurant and down the parking lot ramp. I snapped on my legs and bounded back up to the street level. Those old legs had never felt so good.

Focus on Positive Key to Contentment

♦♦♦

BY

STEPHANE

WUTTUNEE

When I was heavily into weight-lifting years ago, an important virtue my mentors taught was patience. If I were to look in a mirror every day and expect huge results, they'd say I'd quickly become disappointed. Muscle-building is a slow process.

They emphasized significant amounts of progress were best measured in years — not hours, weeks or months. I swore never to forget that lesson.

I have!!

When life goes from smooth sailing to stormy seas, it's easy to get discouraged and list all the things we think would patch us up. How hard it is to be thankful for what we have and can accomplish rather than dwell upon what is lacking or lost.

For myself, I admit the main reason I occasionally dive in melancholic moods (thank God they are rare) results from setting sky-high goals and getting frustrated when they don't materialize quickly enough.

They say we appreciate the good times because of the bad ones. Lord knows how depressed I felt prior to the weekend. You know how it goes, it's the same old story. Young man ponders whether future career plans will work out or not. If so, do they include romance…this and that. Argh. Give me a break.

These useless musings can drag anybody down. I knew therapy was needed. Fast. And it came in a most refreshing way.

I've just returned from chaperoning a camping trip to beautiful Ojibway Park with an enthusiastic group of 55 teenagers from Wellington Junior High School in Sioux Lookout, Ont.

For three days, we fished, hiked trails, listened to loons, called various species of wildlife to us and gazed dreamily into the glowing embers of burning camp-fires at night. And this with the large, cozy interior of my father's tipi as headquarters.

In the evenings, when kids asked Dad serious questions about Native culture, I was pleasantly reminded of my own youthful beginnings in the quest for knowledge. Over the years, I learned to love myself and therefore all living creatures.

We could all learn more from our kin. Immersing myself in a totally synchronized and serene environment was an unbeatable solution to my problem.

Unfortunately, due to today's demands of keeping up the social pace, it isn't always possible to escape to the boonies.

I have fond memories of long winter nights I spent writing at home in Calgary. About what? Absolutely anything that crossed my mind. It didn't matter, so long as I released the pent-up trash in my head.

Just as people weed their gardens, it is equally important we also "weed out" our minds.

This reminds me of a story. A little boy stuck his hand in a gumball machine, trying to get some candies. After some attempts, he succeeded in grasping a few. Yet when his friends came by and tried to get him to come out and play, he found he couldn't follow them. His hand was caught because he still wanted the sweets. He missed the fun his friends were having.

You can only learn from the past. Try hanging on to previous mistakes and your "soul" companions will become despondency, sorrow and grief. It's not worth it. Why waste energy on the negative when there is so much beauty around us?

In this age, what's really nice to know is that no matter how favorable or bad our situations, we are never alone. Though captains of our individual ships, the same oceans bond us.

Gazing out the porch window on the gorgeous sunny morning, memories of the way I was feeling merely days ago now seem puny and unimportant. I have millions of things to be thankful for: good health, a loving family, a burgeoning new writing career — the list goes on.

I'll absorb a lesson from the animals, who never have time to sit around and mope all day — they are too busy living life to the fullest. Now I know what my elders meant when they said to keep the balance.

Guess what, my friends. Life is good.

Legacies

◆◆◆

BY

NIKKI

GIOVANNI

her grandmother called her from the playground
  "yes, ma'am"
  "i want chu to learn how to make rolls" said the old
woman proudly
but the little girl didn't want
to learn how because she knew
even if she couldn't say it that
that would mean when the old one died she would be less
dependent upon her spirit so
she said
  "i don't want to know how to make no rolls"
with her lips poked out
and the old woman wiped her hands on
her apron saying "lord
  these children"
and neither of them ever
said what they meant
and i guess nobody ever does

If I Had
the Wings of
an Angel

♦♦♦

BY

JOE

HALDEMAN

Marianne Scanlan floated in line, feeling sick and nervous and
heavy. This morning the gym scale had weighed her in at
thirty-five kilograms, the cut-off point. She'd gotten rid of breakfast and hadn't drunk anything all morning.

Her turn. She floated up to the scale at the wing rack and grabbed
both handles. Her palms were sweaty. The scale gave a jerk, measur-
ing her inertia, and the wing man looked at the dial, looked at her,
looked back at the dial.

"Thirty-four point nine," he said. He started to say something else
and then just pointed to the end of the rack. Number twelve, the
biggest set. She'd been using it since the first of the year.

She wasn't going to be dumb about it. At thirteen, she was older
than most people were when they hit thirty-five and had their cards
taken away. Boys especially would starve and puke and take laxatives
to keep from putting on those last few grams. But it was ridiculous.
Flying was for kids, and you couldn't stay a kid forever.

She clamped on the ankle vanes and backed into the wing frame.
Right wrist and elbow straps, then carefully draw the huge wing over

to fasten the left side.

Toes push down, release bar clicks, wings at your side, bend at the knees, lean out and fall. The jump platform slipped away behind her.

It always felt the same, launching. Deep inside you, a sudden wrench that wasn't pleasant — your body noticing that you were about to plummet half a kilometer to certain death — and then the weird sparkle of relief rolling to your toes and fingertips. You'd think a girl born and raised in space would grow out of groundhog reflexes. You're not going to fall anywhere, floating off a platform at the zero-G axis. But it was a long way down nevertheless.

She looked at New New York rolling slowly by beneath her, unimpressed by the majesty of it, knowing that groundhogs paid millions to see just this, but knowing that groundhogs do crazy things. She wasn't going fast enough for the wind to bring tears, but the sight blurred anyhow. She dug the tears away with her shoulders, angry with herself. So maybe it's the last time. Probably it's the last time. Don't be an ass about it.

She checked behind her; the next boy hadn't launched yet. Beat hard once, flutter kick, knees to chest, quarter roll, beat hard twice, three times: straight down swoop. Wings at her side, the lake in the middle of the park rushing up at her.

People died doing this. Kids who had their wings but weren't good at it yet. You could hit hard enough to break your neck. Or you could drown.

She hit the thermocline over the lake and the wind sighing by turned deliciously cool. Her cheeks dried cold. Two people in a boat looked up at her, their faces tiny ovals. Far enough.

Legs spread wide, both ankles out, right wing suddenly dipped to a precise angle, legs back together as she looped three, four, five, tight dizzy loops over the water; then kicked and reversed it, left wing sculling to bring her around in wide slow circles. She was going to lose it forever, next week or the next or the next. She let herself cry again and pulled air with both wings, dumping speed, drifting down toward the treetops by the lake's edge, not quite low enough to lose her card — then beat hard, kick hard, climbing with all her might, as the lake rotated away.

Tourists usually found it confusing, even dizzying, to look down from the axis and see all that real estate spinning around. Marianne never thought about it, of course, except for times like now: she idly wondered how fast you'd have to fly to zip through the axis and catch up with the lake as it rolled to the other side. Fast.

Hard to fly and do arithmetic at the same time. She relaxed, ankles together, and glided smoothly. New New York was a hollowed-out asteroid, the hollow being a little more than a kilometer wide and a little less than two kilometers long. It spun around (for gravity) once each thirty second. So you'd have to go a kilometer in fifteen seconds. That's four kilometers per minute; 240 per hour. Not likely to happen. The wings were designed to keep you from going too fast; the strongest kids could go from one side to the other in about three minutes.

A beginner was having problems, slowly tumbling end over end, crying. Eight or nine years old. No danger unless she managed to end up in the water. Still, Marianne could remember how scary it was in the beginning. She beat twice and caught up with the kid.

It was simple. She'd accidentally hit the elbow release on her left wing and couldn't fit her arm back into it. Marianne hit both of her releases (the wings would stay with her unless she undid the ankles) and reached out to grab the girl, stop her spinning.

"I didn't *do* nothin'!" The girl sobbed.

"It's all right." Marianne guided the elbow strap back into the release flange. "Just don't twist your elbow *this* way." She demonstrated, rotating her arm as if she were turning a doorknob stiff-armed. "Not until you want to get out of the wings."

The girl looked doubtful, and gave a couple of tentative flaps. "I'm scared."

"Don't worry. I'll stay with you." She pulled a couple of meters away. "You don't have a buddy?"

She started to cloud up. "She *ditched* me."

"It's okay. Try this: wings straight out, legs stiff." The girl copied her. "Now just give little kicks as if you were swimming."

"Don't know *how* to swim."

"Just do it." Marianne dipped and rolled, to watch her from below. The girl gave a couple of stiff, awkward kicks and then smiled as she glided past Marianne.

"See? Nothing to it. Now I'll show you how to dive." For the rest of her hour Marianne showed the little girl her basic moves and made her learn the names for everything. They were almost to the opposite end of the hub when the buzzer on her shoulder gave its ten-minute warning. Marianne "raced" her back, flying slowly upside-down, and let her win.

She helped the little girl get out of her wings and racked them properly. "Thank you very much," the girl said seriously. "Can we do it again next week?"

"I'm afraid..." Marianne cleared her throat. "I'm afraid I have to go someplace. You know plenty enough, though. Just find a new buddy."

Marianne got her clarinet out of the locker and wiggled her feet into Velcro slippers. She swam hand over hand to the Sector 4 lift and stuck her feet onto the ceiling, automatically making the mental adjustment that turned it into the floor.

It began to slide "down." Two hours to band practice. Better eat something now. If you play a clarinet too soon after eating, the mouthpiece fills up with spit and it sounds like a baby rhinoceros with a cold.

Better eat something. Or maybe not. The lift thumped to a halt and gravity suddenly returned.

She walked down the corridor to the mall and flipped through her ration book. Maybe just a salad. If she starved for a week she could fly again. Probably.

One of the pieces she'd been practicing for bank was a medley of old American spirituals, for an ethnic concert. The words to one of the songs had been nagging her all week, the sad rightness of them: "If I had the wings of an angel, over these prison walls I would fly..."

People from Earth think we live in a prison, she knew, some of them. Rock walls all around us, a bubble of air surrounded by the vast deadly indifference of space.

What they don't see is that gravity is a prison. They live at the bottom of a well. We live inside a rock, but we can fly.

She stopped at the entrance to the mall and studied her ration book.

For five or six years, we can fly.

Cheeseburger. Two cheeseburgers.

The Nest

♦♦♦

BY

ROBERT

ZACKS

immy was fourteen. He was listening to his mother tell him, in her kindly, measured speech, why she didn't want him to go on the hike, and his clear gray eyes were clouded with sullen rebellion.

"All right, Mom," he said in the controlled voice he had learned from his parents. "If you say I can't go, then I can't, can I?"

Mrs. Swanson said gravely, "You make me sound like a dictator, Jimmy."

"Well, you are, kind of, aren't you?" said Jimmy coldly. "I have to do what you say."

His mother winced a little. She bit her lower lip and considered this.

"It isn't as simple as that," she said, pushing her mind with some difficulty toward coping with the point Jimmy had made. She smiled a little, however, in pleasure at such evidence of Jimmy's growing power to analyze a situation. "My decisions are made for your own good, Jimmy."

He misunderstood her smile. He thought she was relegating him to his position as a child. All his parents seemed to do these days was figure out how to hem him in. "Jimmy, you mustn't —"

The words, the restrictions, they wrapped around him like tentacles of an octopus, crushing in on his chest so he couldn't seem to breathe.

He was on his feet, yelling, the controlled, polite speech lost in his bursting anguish for freedom. "Everything is for my own good. Everything! But you aren't telling me the truth. You know why you don't want me to go on the hike? Because of Paul. You just don't like him."

He sucked in his breath, almost sobbing, shocked at himself and yet glad. Mrs. Swanson had an unhappy look. The Swansons were a happy family; but these days a strange restlessness had come into it.

"No," she admitted. "I don't think Paul is good for you. I don't like your associating with him."

Jimmy said, all his heart and soul in his words, "I like Paul. He's my best friend."

"His father is a drunkard," said Mrs. Swanson quietly. "And Paul came out of reform school, didn't he? He stole from a candy store —"

"He's *nice!*" cried Jimmy, pain in his voice. "And he isn't a crook. He made a mistake. He told me what happened. He was showing off. And now nobody will be friends —"

"But he's formed a gang already, hasn't he? I've heard about it."

"It's just a club, that's all," said Jimmy. "And — and I'm a member. The club is running the hike."

"We won't discuss it further." Mrs. Swanson's voice was suddenly like steel. She stood up. She hesitated, pitying him, and tried to soften it with logic. "Remember, Jimmy, every time we've disagreed, it turned out I knew what I was talking about."

But he didn't listen further. Jimmy turned and blindly ran off the porch across the lawn toward the meeting place at Briggs' Drugstore.

After three blocks he slowed down, panting, his face set with fury. The habit of thinking, encouraged by his parents at every opportunity, began to function.

"'I know what's best for you. I know what's best for you.' That's all I ever hear!" muttered Jimmy.

To his reluctant mind sprang memories. The time he insisted he could swim to the raft. Mr. Swanson had curtly said no, he couldn't risk it. Jimmy had raged, with his father quietly letting him run down. Then his father had told him to go ahead, but that he'd swim next to him.

Jimmy's throat strangled suddenly at the memory: the water was constricting his windpipe dreadfully, his eyes were bulging, his legs and arms numb with exhaustion from the too-long swim. And then the wonderful, strong, blessed arms of his father turning him on his back, pulling him back to shore —

It was confusing. Jimmy shook his head in bewilderment. Suddenly he felt uncertain, the rebellion drained out of him.

Paul was waiting for him at the drugstore with a stillness upon his face as he leaned against the glass front. He was about fourteen, with dark hair and bright dark eyes. He wore dungarees. Jimmy saw, when he came closer, traces of tears on Paul's cheeks.

"Well," said Paul fiercely, "let's go."

Jimmy started. "Where's everybody?"

"They changed their minds," said Paul, hate in his voice.

The two boys looked at each other, and Jimmy understood. It made fury grow in him, it made him want to hit somebody. All those parents had stopped the gang from going with Paul because he was once in a reform school.

Paul said, his voice odd, "Maybe you can't go either?"

Jimmy looked deep into Paul's eyes. His heart beat fast with friendship and loyalty. "Don't be a jerk. Come on," he said cheerfully.

Paul's face changed. The hate seeped away, leaving sweetness and humbleness. He flung an arm over Jimmy's shoulder happily.

"Your — your mother doesn't care if you go, huh?" he said.

Jimmy swallowed. Paul needed this so badly. So very badly. Paul had no mother at all. And his father just didn't like looking at the world without Paul's mother, and was always drunk.

"Nah," said Jimmy. "She — she even said I should bring you to supper, afterwards. What shall I tell her, huh?"

Paul turned ashen, then flushed a deep scarlet. "Sure," he muttered. "Be glad to."

"I got to call her," said Jimmy numbly. "Just a minute."

Jimmy went into the drugstore and called his mother. He told her in a choking voice he was going on the hike, just he and Paul, and he didn't care how mad she got. "Nobody else came," he shouted into the telephone, "because all the mothers —" He was unable to go on for a moment. Then he finished. "I'm bringing him to supper afterwards, Mom. I said you asked him."

He hung up before she could answer.

They had a wonderful day. Wonderful. It was May, and the leaves on the trees were chartreuse and new. They went six miles out of town. They watched chipmunks skitter. They lay on their backs and stared at fleecy white clouds changing shape. Paul's face showed his contentment. His eyes were dreamy.

But Jimmy, in one cloud, saw the stern face of his mother.

But Mrs. Swanson's face, when she greeted Paul, wasn't stern at all. She looked uncertain as she studied his wistful, shy smile. Jimmy knew, of course, that his parents would wait until later to lecture him. They never made a scene before other people.

Throughout supper, Mr. Swanson was very friendly to their guest. But Jimmy could see that at the same time his father was carefully studying Paul. And Paul, never knowing, thinking they'd wanted him, had invited him, glowed and showed the side of his personality that Jimmy liked.

After they'd washed the dishes (at Paul's suggestion), Mr. Swanson nodded to Paul. "Come on, Paul," he said. "I'll show you my tool shop."

As Paul eagerly followed him down the basement steps, Mrs. Swanson touched Jimmy's shoulder. Jimmy's heart thudded as he reluctantly lingered behind. He turned and glared in defiance.

"I don't care," he whispered. "Nobody else came. I couldn't —"

"Jimmy," she said softly, and bent and kissed him. "I'm proud of you, Jimmy. You did the right thing at the right time."

"But you said —" faltered Jimmy. "I mean —"

Her eyes were very bright. "I was wrong," she said steadily. "This time I was wrong. You were right. He's a nice boy, I think."

She turned away, patting his cheek as she did so.

At first, joy filled Jimmy. Joy and pride. *I'm the one who's right,* he thought, dazed. *My mother was wrong. Actually wrong. She admitted it.*

And then came a queer and frightening sense of loss, as well as of gain. It was like being alone, high up on a precipice where the footing was slippery with moss. Jimmy felt he had to be careful of each step. He had always been sure, even in his anger, of being able to depend on the wisdom of his father and mother. They'd always been right.

But not any more. Now they *might* be wrong. And Jimmy would have to decide.

The Boy,
the Balloon,
and Open Blue

◆◆◆

BY

**HEATHER HAAS
BARCLAY**

When the boy came to the new country he brought only his knife. The knife had belonged to his grandfather for many years.

"We cannot carry much in our arms," the boy's mother said. "We will remember."

The boy's grandparents were too old to start again in the new country. They hugged the boy and said he needed to be free. When they were young, they told him, they had been free to go anywhere.

But the boy wanted to stay behind with his grandparents who had cared for him while his parents worked in the city.

"Perhaps," the boy's father said, "when we have made enough money to buy a fine house, your grandson will learn to fly an airplane and he will come back for you."

The boy nodded hard.

The grandparents rocked gently. They smiled and their cheeks squeezed round and red.

"Perhaps," they said, standing up at the same time.

"We have heard," the boy's grandmother said, "going to the new country takes a long time." She brought the boy's parents bread and cheeses for the journey. She gave the boy's mother seeds for her garden.

His grandfather closed the boy's fingers around the knife, the same knife he had used to whittle wooden birds for the boy.

When the boy's parents returned to their room in the city they gave the food away because they could not carry it with them. The boy's mother put seeds for sunflowers, cucumbers, squash and pumpkins in the hems of her skirts.

The boy thought the seeds had spoiled as the family slept in crowded rooms, sat on damp trains, and stood in long lines waiting for bread, blankets and official stamps on the papers they won by outwaiting others. Finally, the man from the new country spoke to his father and told him the boy's family had permission to leave.

From behind high wire fences the others watched the boy going. His mother and his father held his hands. They did not look back. In the open blue the boy felt as though the plane stayed still while the world unrolled like a sacred silver scroll.

When they arrived his mother carefully undid her hems to uncover the seeds. She pinched each one like a miser counting coins, then placed them on mismatched plates according to their variety.

"We will be at home here," she said to the seeds.

The boy spread his arms to measure the space of his own room, the space from his room to the bathroom, the space in the kitchen, the front porch, the backyard.

The seeds his mother planted grew. Sunflowers shielded the porch. Squash blossoms hung from cedars at the driveway and cucumbers like fingers clutched and pulled on the little carpet of grass in the backyard.

Warm summer evenings, the boy and his parents sat on their porch on a couch they had found beside a curb. Neighbours mowed their lawns, clipped their hedges, weeded and swept, talking louder than necessary, occasionally throwing their eyes at the strangers on the legless couch on the porch. The boy's mother would go inside and stir the large pot she had carried to the new country. The boy's father slept briefly before leaving again for his second job.

At times neighbour boys gathered in front of his house. With shouts and whoops they would return to the street, crisscrossing their bikes in quick arcs. Once, a boy came toward the porch to speak to him. He looked straight into the boy's eyes, as if the boy could understand. But he spoke full of roaring sounds like busy traffic. When the boy did not reply, he went back to his friends, jumped on the seat of another boy's bike to show how two could ride at once. But the boy was afraid to let anyone take him anywhere farther than where he was.

One morning the boy heard a distant sound, velvety shooshing in the open blue. He stood on his porch, searched the sky and saw a rainbow balloon floating toward him. As the balloon approached he could see two people, no bigger than his mother's sunflower seeds, standing inside a wicker basket attached to the beautiful balloon. The tiny black shapes waved to the boy. Running along under the balloon's path, the boy waved back. The boy ran until the river that wandered through the city stopped him.

After the balloon had shushed into a tiny speck, the boy stayed in a field full of lace and daisies and purple-tailed flowers. He sat for a long time at the river's edge. There he watched ducks skid in to swim and otters somersault; he heard crows curse.

Every day he returned to the field.

He sat by the river, sometimes whittling branches with his knife, remembering the owls, the bluebirds, the swallows his grandfather carved while the boy had lived with him. Here the boy discovered many secrets: Heron's, as he waited to beak-spear a fish struggling in the shallows; Dragonfly's, stitching her needle body through the air; Starling's, watching flat-footed ducks preen; Fish's secret, hurtling into shrinking sunlight on a quiet evening. And Sky's too, always changing, filling and folding with clouds, trailing streamers of planes, buttoning designs of stars, sweeping storms into swelling monsters that shrivelled like genies into polished blue bottles.

One day, the boy watched green light and grey rainsheets wrap the world outside his window. After the thunder shushed itself, rumbling only now and then like hunger, the boy walked through the wet streets to his river field. The sun seemed to shake itself awake and the grass and flowers sleepily stretched up again too.

By the river, under a willow tree, the boy found a long branch and beside it three young swallows still in a nest. The nestlings' mouths stayed open, their heads tilted back, and each time an adult swallow swooped by their bodies bounced. Reaching to a fork in the willow, the boy gently set the nest in place. Then away he walked, carrying the branch.

The boy thought the branch long enough to be a walking stick, but when he leaned on it, it bent. The boy noticed irregular little lines along the bark and as he was pretending they were magic runes the boy felt eyes behind him. He turned and recognized the adult swallow watching from her perch beside the nest. Then she flew from the branch to climb into the sky. Above the boy she soared, her body and wings pointed.

Like an arrowhead, the boy thought. He held his branch up, bending it carefully into a bow, and he imagined how he might shoot magic arrows through the open blue to land in the hard-packed dirt of his grandparents' yard.

The boy whittled an arrow, then one more every day and on each one he carved a secret he had learned since arriving in the new country. Every day he aimed them way up into the sky across the river. As the boy carved more and more arrows, sometimes he did not want to shoot them away. But the boy wanted to spell his home more than he wanted to keep his carvings.

The sunflowers in the boy's garden began to bow their haloed heads.

"Soon you will not be so alone," his mother said, "you will go to school and learn about this new country."

The boy thought how he would be made to stay inside amid speech he did not understand and people he did not know. Instead of a beautiful arrow, the boy hacked a rough stick, pointed and full of splinters and shot it into the sky. He marched to the willow and pulled the empty nest out of the tree, stepped on it and pitched the pieces into the river. When the boy turned around he saw the swallow perched where the nest had been, cocking her head at him. For the first time since he arrived in the new country the boy wept.

Looking up into the sky the boy watched the swallow pierce higher and higher. Far away the boy could see the balloon that he had chased to the river. It floated toward him, its dragon breathing sound louder, the two specks in the basket bigger and the rainbow colours brighter. Too late, the boy thought, too late.

"Help," the boy heard faintly.

The balloon seemed to approach more quickly and the dragon breathing increased. The fire jet shooting into the rainbow colours panted. The boy could see that the two people were waving hurriedly at him.

"Help," they called out together. "Oh help us, help."

Then the balloon was coming down so quickly it seemed to be falling. The boy guessed that because of the willows and the balloon's quick descent the people needed help to find a landing spot. From his pocket the boy pulled the large handkerchief his mother made him carry and waved it at the people.

"Here, over here," the boy called, "you can land over here." The boy jumped up and down in the field.

The boy could see a piece of the rainbow had torn away from the balloon. As it made its way down, bouncing gently as it landed on the grass beside the boy, the swallow swooped by him.

"An arrow pierced our balloon," the woman said. Her blue-black hair, the way she almost scolded, reminded the boy of starlings at the river. She leaned over the wicker side to throw out an anchor. "You don't know anyone who might have shot it?" she asked.

The boy hid the bow behind his back.

"We always caught them before," the man said, holding up a bundle of arrows exactly like those the boy had shot into the sky, "but this one came so fast and its shaft was so rough, I could not stop it."

They spoke in the boy's language, their words leaping like deer, in the manner of the boy's grandparents.

"And now," the woman pulled on the lapels of her vest thick with embroidered dragonflies, "what can we do?"

The man stood very still watching as the silk of the rainbow balloon fell across the drying stacks of lace and milkweed.

All of a sudden the boy knew. "I will help you," he said.

The man nodded. The smell of carnations and dried leaves in the soap his grandfather used and the wood shavings snagged on his pants and socks — these the boy smelled.

"I can bring a needle and strong thread, scissors and patching material." His mother never threw away any of their worn clothes. The boy returned to the field with the things as quickly as he thought to fetch them.

The woman ripped the sleeve out of the lilac blouse the boy brought. She placed it over the seam and the man began to stitch around it. He sewed standing up, leaning forward from the waist holding the needle in one hand, a piece of the purple patch in the other.

As quickly as the boy wondered when the repair would be done it was finished. The man broke the thread with his teeth, smiling lopsidedly at the boy. While the young woman stretched the strength of the patch, the man climbed into the basket and stood patiently, looking down at the boy.

The boy nodded goodbye, backing up out of the way, his bow still behind him.

But the man interpreted the boy's nod another way, and after climbing into the wicker basket he held up his hands like a heron testing its wings for flight. The woman and the boy reached for his hands and the man pulled them into the balloon basket.

The dragon breathing machine blew hard into the collapsed rainbow silk. The boy watched it swell, feeling the anchor jolt the basket as the young woman placed it in the corner. From that same corner she bent to pick up the boy's last arrow, the one that had torn the balloon. She snapped it over her knee and threw the pieces out on the grass. The balloon began to rise.

To the boy the air had the quick coolness of early morning, and as the balloon rose the earth beneath seemed brittle. He wished he could throw the bow over the side, but the woman slipped it out of his hand very gently.

One by one she carefully shot his bundle of arrows toward the sun. With each shot the balloon rose higher and higher.

Even though the balloon took them high up the boy could see details of his house when he looked down. Sparrows perched on the sunflowers eating out the seeds. His mother stood in their kitchen putting cucumbers in glass jars. His father peeked under leaf flaps at pumpkins and ripening squash. The boys on the street biked by his house waving at his father, calling his name. His neighbourhood, the boy could see, was not so huge.

Higher still the boy saw the whole city. Tiny people pushed baby strollers, strode quickly along the sidewalks, swinging briefcases, sauntered lazily looking in shop windows, and through it all the river ribboned like the drifting tail of a kite. This new city, the boy discovered, was not so huge.

Higher into the open blue they floated. His grandfather was there whittling with a new knife, his grandmother rolling out dough. They waved. The boy saw that they winked as they always did when they were proud. The boy saw the edges of the world sloping gently like the bank of the river by his field.

The woman had shot every one of the arrows the boy had carved. With their hands on the sides of the basket the man and woman gazed down as the balloon began to drift toward the earth. Below them the boy saw his arrows also changing direction, returning to the world.

One by one the arrows pierced the trees below and the leaves turned into gold, red, orange, yellow. The colours of tanned faces and outdoor work, of scrubbing hands and apples, of shined shoes and Sundays, of chatter, woodsmoke, of fresh pencils, of season's change. And the boy saw how he changed. He would walk to school, wave to the boys on bikes, even climb on a bike with one to ride double into the school yard. And at this school he would learn all about this new country. He would remember too. The world, after all, was not that huge.

To Open the
World

♦♦♦

BY

**KAREN
CONNELLY**

*When I was seventeen, I left Calgary. "I'm going
away," I told people, deliberately edging my voice
with mystery. I read certain entries in encyclopedias
and books about foreign lands; Karen Blixen's* Out of
Africa *literally quickened my heartbeat. I went to a
doctor to stock up on malaria pills and receive shots
for diphtheria and hepatitis. My departure date was
at the end of August: all that summer I felt breath-
less, hopeful, and terrified. While walking along the
Bow River on certain warm evenings, I watched the
reflections of trees and rocks dance over the black
water. The sound of the river made me think of Asia.*

I knew the country of my destination, Thailand, could be a very
wet place. I'd seen photographs of the monsoons in Bangkok.
Old Siam, known in eighteenth-century Europe as "the Venice
of the Orient," endures its rainy season every year; the flooding in the
lowlands floats up whole villages. I knew I would be living on fairly
high ground in a small northern town called Denchai, where I would
become part of a Thai family; they would treat me as one of their own.
I would go to a Thai school, eat Thai food, wear Thai clothes; learn to
speak, read, dance, cook Thai. Genuinely kind gentlemen in expensive

business suits explained all of this to me. They were Rotarians and I was a Rotary Exchange Student. In Canada, my mission seemed very clear: I was to become as completely Thai as possible. Through this transformation, I was to learn what it meant to live not simply in my own country but in my own world.

When I left Canada I was crying, fitful and sad, thinking about plane crashes and fatal accidents in foreign lands. I was in love and I didn't want to leave him. Yet I did want to leave, needed to leave, because I'd grown up restlessly, flipping the pages of the *National Geographic,* continually telling myself that I'd — go away someday — escape. Even before I arrived there, Thailand became the world to me, came to symbolize the beginning of my real life, my new life, my own. Rising over the Rockies, those great giants of stone with their blue-green veins and aquamarine sockets of ice water, I vowed that never again would I be shackled by polynomial equations and certain pig-headed teachers. I said to myself, "This is the beginning, because I'm leaving it behind, I'm going." Then I blew my nose furiously and bid the mountains goodbye.

My life in Denchai began in the middle of the night. Like everywhere else in the north, it had, apparently, just stopped raining. When we drove through the puddles in the street, I had the impression that we might never completely surface. I was afraid the water would come into the car. We eventually pulled up in front of the building which was my new home. It was a liquor store. The top floors were for the family: my two small Thai brothers, my Thai mother and father, my Thai aunt, and my Thai grandparents. An enormous German shepherd was kept on a thick chain in the back of the house, which was also the kitchen and the garage. That first night, everyone was asleep except the dog, who obviously didn't like foreigners. All hackles and vicious teeth, she lunged at me again and again while my new Thai father smiled jovially and pulled up a vestige of his long-forgotten English, "Velly nice dog!" I was led up to a room on the top floor. My Thai father left me. I sat down on my very hard bed and howled, as quietly as possible, into my hands.

I was the only foreigner in town, and I was a girl. This combination fascinated the townspeople. Initially, I was treated as a spectacle, the only attraction in a small zoo. Those first days, when "aunt" Pee-Moi showed me how to wash clothes by hand and eat with chopsticks, the children of Denchai came on their ramshackle bicycles and leaned over the handlebars, staring at me from the street and giggling when I greeted them with *"Sawatdee kaa."* The only way I could entice them

to come close to me was by tempting them with photographs. My sister, who has long blonde hair, especially delighted them. They thought my younger brother looked like James Dean. The candy I brought for them — licorice Goodies — caused a stir. They liked the bright colours but thought the dark brown filling looked exactly like lizard excrement. I met Lin, Deh, Boh, and Sak those first days, all of them between the ages of fifteen and seventeen. They later became some of my closest friends.

Within two days, still afflicted by jet lag and just noticing the effects of the new food on my stomach, I was at Nareerat School in the small city of Prae, twenty-five kilometres from Denchai. Over three thousand students, almost all of them girls, came from many of the small towns and villages in the province to attend Nareerat. When I first walked into the compound of those apple-green buildings, hundreds of pretty girls with gleaming black hair leaned over the second- and third-floor balconies to watch my passage. They giggled behind their hands. Some threw roses. I was the only white student in the school.

I began my life in Thailand wearing a Thai school girl's starched white blouse, pleated blue skirt, and patent leather Mary Janes with bobby socks. At first, this uniform mortified me, but eventually I became reconciled to everything but the Mary Janes. I hated those toe-cramming black shoes every time I put them on. (Fortunately, we always took our shoes off before entering a room, so I spent most of the day in stocking or bare feet.) The uniform helped by camouflaging me a little. I needed to become a Thai girl, and was obliged to accept many rigid traditions, even if I didn't agree with them. I came to appreciate the Canadian confusion over culture. I'm glad Canada has no specific, defined culture, because I've experienced the restrictions of living in a society which does.

But I also experienced the benefits of those old traditions. I became a real part of a real community — something I'd never experienced in Calgary. Within a couple of months, I knew hundreds of people in Denchai and Prae, waved to them in the street, chatted, smiled. The Thai smile — *yim siam* — is a Thai characteristic. In Thailand, I learned how much people really do communicate through facial expression and laughter was my first Thai sound.

I studied voraciously. Thai is a tonal language of over seventy alphabetical characters which resemble spermatozoa in motion: all twirls, loops, and squiggles. A beautiful script, but very difficult to write. I concentrated on the five different tones and all the words which compromised daily living and communicating. I carried a notebook of phonetic lists around and pestered people with the constant question, *"Cheuh allai nee, na ka?"* "What is this called?" I practised with my friends at the badminton court where we met every day after school (and where, for an entire year, I lost every game I played). I worked hard at my Thai, sometimes even desperately. The need to communicate became one of my primary drives because I was deeply lonely. Though I'd performed the operation myself, I'd been amputated from Canada, from my friends, and especially from my language, which I'd always used to define myself. As I struggled to remember the words "hand" and "face" and "sky," I realized that losing English was easily comparable to losing a limb. One of my dozen Thai fathers (all members of the Denchai Rotary Club) spoke English but I only saw him once a week. To everyone else in Denchai, English was gibberish. Until I could rename the world in Thai, I was handicapped.

Even after plunging deep into that beautiful singing language, learning hundreds, thousands of new words, I knew English was still my real voice, and Alberta was the place where that voice had first grown and learned something of itself. I dreamed of snow in Thailand; I dreamed of hiking in the Kananaskis, of canoeing the Sheep River. In the morning, driving to Prae in the back of an open truck, careening through the green glimmer and silver sheen of rice paddies, I looked to the northern mountains and thought: those are hills. I know what real mountains look like and they are nothing like those stubby things.

Yet I never tired of my adopted country's landscape. It was wild, tropical, constantly growing, changing, forever new. A four-inch long, lime-green praying mantis lived in my bedroom. A large striped lizard lived in Pee-Moi's rose garden. The butterflies were bigger than my hands and I followed them from flower to flower with unhinged jaws. Their wings were bright red, green, purple, blue. As a child I'd painted such fanciful butterflies, imagining they might exist on some brighter planet. In the mornings, I was often greeted by red-shelled beetles scrambling around the sink; they came up the drains. Under my desk, I once found a tiny baby lizard, a mere wisp of dark green, so delicate and small that I wanted to close it in a book and press it like a flower.

I loved living in Denchai and exploring the surrounding countryside because it always gifted me with surprises. Once Deh and Boh and I flew over the narrow field roads on noisy motorcycles, passing through miniature jungles and hamlets of waving children and flapping chickens. We almost killed ourselves several times by swerving into deep wagon ruts; we were trying to avoid running over sunning snakes. Domesticated water buffalo watched us flash by their deep pools of mud. After roaring through groves of coconut, teak, and bamboo, we arrived at a whitewashed temple in the middle of nowhere. Not a village anywhere nearby, not a soul to be seen in all the blue-green world, but there was a deep clay basin of water and a high-ceilinged temple. Its walls were painted with colourful depictions of Buddha's life, its floor was cool beneath our feet. We padded up to the image of the Enlightened One, knelt, and bowed three times in respect. We drank some water, then sat in the shadows and marveled at the painted ceiling. After a while, we left the temple and traveled north, clattered over a narrow swinging bridge, then stopped to swim in the river below. By the time I arrived home late in the afternoon, I'd felt I'd traveled half the circumference of the Earth.

In many ways, I had. Denchai, whose name no one would know if the Bangkok train didn't pass through twice a day, taught me that countries are constellations connected by invisible lines. Those connections create a greater picture of who and what we are as human beings. I learned about history in Southeast Asia; I learned how the lens of the past clouds and deepens our vision of the future. Talking with old people in an old country teaches these things. Canada became young to me when I discovered how ancient Thailand was. One of my older teachers once said, "I hope you will be patient. Thailand is like an old man, hard to reason with, tough as a sun-dried shoe. You come from a country that still has the skin of a child...."

June rolled into July, and I stood on the top floor of the shop looking out at the busy streets of my town, the pedlars bobbing along under their loads of grapes and pineapples, the people on bicycles, entire families packed onto motorcycles. I pressed my fingers against the tattered screen on the window, thinking, "Next month is August. A year. I'm going back to Canada." I shivered despite the heat. Thinking about Canada occasionally made me happy but I was not looking forward to returning. My love of the previous year had dissolved during the course of my stay; he was now living with a librarian. I had to go back to Calgary and make some decisions about the future. I knew I wanted to write a book about living in Thailand; I knew I wanted to be a writer, felt I was a writer already, but I needed to learn the discipline of my craft. The Thais laughed when they saw me scribbling in my notebook, laughed even harder when I explained that I was writing

about them. They thought I was ridiculous, and though I often agreed with them, I continued writing everything down.

Yes, I was leaving. I packed. I had delicious dinners. A party was thrown in my honour. I made a speech to the students and teachers of Nareerat, all those black heads in the assembly field, those faces watching me curiously, affectionately, as they had all year. So many people had befriended me, participated in educating my Western barbarism. The smallest children had taught me the national anthem, a song I'd loved even the first time I'd heard it. I packed my clothes, my treasure of Thai silver, my silk dress, my lapis luzuli necklace, my notebooks. People gave me orchids, roses, lilies. I wept. Some of my friends cried, too. I was going away, and Canada seemed like the most distant country on Earth.

I left Asia just as I left North America: sobbing, searching for Kleenex while my green country was yanked out from under me. I slept for a few hours while flying over the Pacific. While transferring planes in Seattle, I started crying again because all the people were big, white, and looked alike; they all had pale hair, bony faces, big bodies. I missed Thailand and I deeply missed the Thais. Every time I opened my mouth, Thai came out of it. "Thank you" was *"Cop koon kaa"* and "Pardon me?" turned into *"Allai na ka?"*

Calgary was no better. I was happy to see my family and friends again but I missed Thailand more than I'd missed Canada, perhaps because I'd worked so hard to love it. In Calgary, people didn't greet me and smile on the street; people weren't interested in me. After all, I was part of a white majority; I wasn't interesting any more. The neighbourhood I lived in seemed to just be row on row of ugly condos full of people who worked in offices all day and didn't want to make any new friends. I thought, how cold these people are, how dull; they wear gray and black clothes and no one carries around a guitar. I longed for the easy familiarity I had had with so many people in Denchai and Prae.

I began to stop unsuspecting Asian people on the street, the buses, in shopping markets, in malls. "Excuse me," I would say, "are you Thai?" I inquired matter-of-factly, as if asking for the time. They always laughed and said, no, I'm Filipino, or Cambodian, or Vietnamese, or Indonesian. I started tutoring Asian students at a local high school. We traded stories about living in an adopted country; they experienced many of the things I'd experienced in Thailand. Newspapers were mysterious. The television was peopled by voices which might have been transmitted from Mars. Using public transportation became a matter of blind luck. The world suddenly became strange. One young Vietnamese girl was shocked when she saw her first turkey. "I never knew chickens, even Canadian chickens, could get that big." I spent hours teaching the pronunciation and meanings of words like beach and bitch, wild and while, steel and still, and many of the frustrating homonyms of English. "Why can we say 'to sweeten' but not 'to colden' and 'to heaten'? And why does 'marked' turn back into 'mark' but 'naked' never turns into 'nake'? English is much harder than Vietnamese." I started studying Vietnamese with some of my students. I listened to Thai music every day and read books about China.

When an acquaintance of mine told me about a Thai woman she knew, I was overjoyed. I called Ling immediately and spoke Thai for an hour, grinning the entire time. Through Ling I discovered a small Thai community in Calgary and managed to keep speaking Thai. It wasn't the same as being in Denchai but it eased the transition for me. These Thais had become Canadian, and all of them preferred Canada to Thailand, enjoyed living in Alberta, being close to the mountains and the prairies. One Thai-Canadian said, "The sky is higher here. I like that. And I come from Bangkok, big dirty city. It's clean here. I like Thailand, but I live here now, and if I leave, I know I'll return. It's my home."

I slowly discovered the same is true for me. Though I've since left and lived in another foreign country, and though I'll leave again, I know that something here will always call me back. This place, too, is a point in the constellation, part of the painting of an extraordinary, open world.

Learning
for
Life

♦ ♦ ♦

Go to school. Graduate. Get a good job. Advance in the company. Retire.

Sound like a good plan? Wrong. What worked for past generations isn't good enough in a world of rapid technological change and global competitiveness.

Futurists predict people entering the workforce today will have to change jobs five or six times during their lifetime. Even to stay in the same job, you'll have to gain new skills to keep up with changing technology. For instance, service stations are finding it difficult to get enough skilled workers who understand the electronic machinery used to find out what's wrong with and repair the vehicles of the 1990s.

That means you must always be prepared to pick up new knowledge and skills. It means making a commitment to life-long learning.

Take a tip from Brenda Lamha, who has held several jobs over the years ranging from truck driver to floral designer.

Driving a truck was a childhood ambition, so she enrolled in a driving school to get her Class One licence. She got a job right away, but was laid off three years later.

She then landed a job as a floral designer, a skill she had picked up, during a period of unemployment, through on-the-job training coupled with in-class hours at Olds College.

"I believe that when I'm one hundred years old if I want to learn something more, I'll be going out and learning it," Lamha says. She's now considering going back to school for a change to an as-yet-undecided new career.

Your Ticket to Tomorrow's Job Market: Make Sure These Words Apply to You

Mathematics Skills

Science skills

Computer skills

Communication skills

Team playing skills

Life-long learning

Flexibility

Self-motivation

Customer focus

Mobility

Multi-skilled

Technically proficient

Ability to take responsibility

Innovativeness

Risk taking

Entrepreneurial skills

New Ways to Work

The rigid 40-hour workweek portioned out into five 8-hour days is going the way of the dinosaur. For many reasons, including personal lifestyle choices, technology and economic realities, flexibility is the trademark of the '90s workplace.

Here are some of the new ways employers and employees are choosing to schedule their work time.

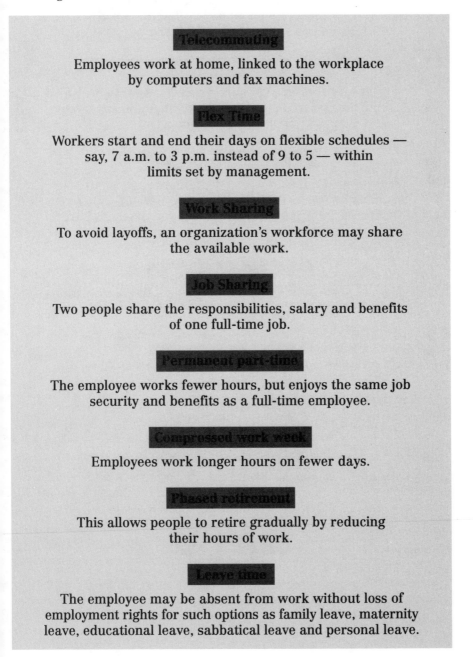

Telecommuting

Employees work at home, linked to the workplace by computers and fax machines.

Flex Time

Workers start and end their days on flexible schedules — say, 7 a.m. to 3 p.m. instead of 9 to 5 — within limits set by management.

Work Sharing

To avoid layoffs, an organization's workforce may share the available work.

Job Sharing

Two people share the responsibilities, salary and benefits of one full-time job.

Permanent part-time

The employee works fewer hours, but enjoys the same job security and benefits as a full-time employee.

Compressed work week

Employees work longer hours on fewer days.

Phased retirement

This allows people to retire gradually by reducing their hours of work.

Leave time

The employee may be absent from work without loss of employment rights for such options as family leave, maternity leave, educational leave, sabbatical leave and personal leave.

It's a Fact

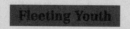
Fleeting Youth

The youth population will continue to decline from 23 per cent of the Canadian population in 1976 to 13 per cent by 2001 and to about 11 per cent by the year 2031.

The Training Gap

The average worker in Canada receives seven hours of training per year compared with 200 hours in Japan and 170 hours in Sweden.

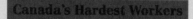
Canada's Hardest Workers

The average Canadian works 38.3 hours a week, an hour more than he or she did seven years ago. About 18 per cent of Albertans and Prince Edward Islanders, Canada's hardest workers, put in more than 50 hours a week.

Where Do the Hours Go?

The average executive spends two hours a day simply trying to reach people on the telephone and another two hours a day in meetings.

Dropping Out

About 30 per cent of high school students in Canada drop out despite the increasing demand for workers with higher levels of education.

No Place Like Home

In Canada's four western provinces, 71 per cent of all new jobs in 1990 were home-based. Statistics Canada estimates there are now almost 1 200 000 home-based businesses in Canada.

Finishing School

The American Society of Training and Development estimates that 20 per cent of a person's employment income is a result of completing high school, and some 80 per cent of earning potential comes from a commitment to upgrading, training and self-development.

Not a Baaaaad Occupation

Number of spaces available in a 17-week training course for shepherds at Okanagan College in British Columbia: 15. Number of would-be shepherds who applied for a space: 250.
— Courtesy of Warren Clements, *Report on Business*

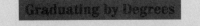

Graduating by Degrees

Percentage of males/females receiving degrees in Canada:

Bachelors	1961:	72.5 male/27.5 female
	1991:	43.9 male/56.1 female
Masters	1961:	83 male/17 female
	1991:	52.2 male/47.8 female
Doctorates	1961:	91.9 male/8.1 female
	1991:	66.8 male/33.2 female

— Source: Statistics Canada

They Get No Satisfaction

A Canadian Federation of Independent Business survey reveals that 58 per cent of its members are unsatisfied with the way high schools prepare students for the labor market.

Information by the Truckload

The information that mechanics needed in 1962 to repair trucks was contained in about 5000 pages. Now, the basic information is 45 000 pages with technological advances adding another 1000 pages a year.

Forklift Poem/Winter

♦♦♦

BY

NICK

MUSKA

When I drive lift
   I am saddled to a peeled-paint rhino
   who would charge concrete and crumble block
   If I did not hold it tightly by the ears.

When I drive lift
   I raise three ton with my right hand
   and can tilt, spin, drop it
   like a plumed lead hat.

When I drive lift
   I am the slave of capital, bleeding hydraulic sweat
   and oil in airless semi-trailers, blue-toed
   froze to the gas pedal, gritty.

When I drive lift
  I have a handle on the nuts and bolts of things
  pirouetting with iron castings in my jaws
  lost without thought.

When I drive lift
  From my rhino perch I am lord of all I survey:
  An iron-dark, echo-empty warehouse
  Ben's junkyard next door, its soil gone oil
  sun glinting hard from stacks of rear-view mirrors.

When I drive lift
  I am the last snorting thing left out on the dock
  breath and exhaust lost in the snowstorm
  blowing under the edge of the overhead doors.

Sylvia Earle in The Deep Rover submersible

Champion of the Deep

♦♦♦

BY

PEGGY

ORENSTEIN

A mile off the Florida Keys, and 80 feet [24 m] down, the silence is thicker and more majestic than anywhere on land. There is no splash of surf, no whisper of wind, no hum of insect or avian life. There is only the long, rhythmic pull of air from our scuba tanks as we glide past the complicated tangles of coral and gently waving sea fans of Molasses Reef. At this depth, reds and yellows begin to fade and darker colors take on the richness of twilight. Below us, a six-foot-long iridescent green eel blocks the entrance to his coral cave, watching until we are safely out of sight. To the left, the reef rolls down into darkness, into what is literally — even to the most experienced divers, who generally go no more than about 100 to 150 feet [30 to 45 m] deep — the unfathomable.

I try to imagine diving untethered to 1250 feet [375 m], the recordbreaking depth to which the woman I am with, Dr. Sylvia A. Earle, has ventured. The chief scientist of the National Oceanic and Atmospheric Administration and one of the world's foremost divers, Earle was also one of the first three pilots to take a one-person submersible vessel to a depth of 3000 feet [900 m].

And now she hopes to reach and explore one day soon the deepest-known point in the ocean, a very, very dark 35 800 feet [10 740 m]. This is the depth to which she believes marine science must sink in order to understand, and preserve, this planet.

While most of us call home the 33 percent of the earth above the shoreline, Sylvia Earle thrives at the lower depths. At 55, she has logged more than 5000 hours under the sea as an aquanaut and marine biologist, including a two-week continuous stint in 1970, discovering and cataloguing previously unknown species of marine life. Admirers have christened both ocean critters and plants in her name (divers may chance upon the sea urchin *Diadema sylvie* or the underwater plant *Pilina earli).*

"People are under the impression that the planet is fully explored," she says of her journeys to inner space, "that we've been to all the forests and climbed all the mountains. But in fact many of the forests have yet to be seen for the first time. They just happen to be underwater. We're still explorers. Perhaps the greatest era is just beginning."

It is generally accurate to precede Earle's achievements with the label "first woman" — as in first woman to be chief scientist at the National Oceanic and Atmospheric Administration (NOAA) — but that mitigates their significance. For *anyone* to have racked up as many laurels as Earle has is remarkable. The fact that she has done so at a time when female scientists continue to be denied research opportunities (and were until recently considered bad luck on a boat) simply gives her success extra resonance....

"Everyone says that they have these childhood memories of blue oceans and green grass and trees and that now things aren't what they used to be," she says as we drive through the groves of drought-browned Eucalyptus covering northern California. "And that's not just the early childhood perspective. There aren't trees where there used to be. Oceans aren't as blue. I grew up in Clearwater, Fla., which doesn't live up to its name anymore. And it's all happened so fast — *geological* time has become something that happens in lifetimes. We've burned through our resources thinking there's always more, but the world has become suddenly small. We have to start recognizing that it's all one system and it's in our own best interests to take care of the place."

Earle's entire life has been oriented toward the ocean — she began diving at 17, using a helmet, compressed air and weights to explore the bottom of a Florida riverbed. A few years later, while working toward a degree in marine botany at Florida State, she was among the early devotees of scuba — which was invented in 1943 — always with an eye toward going deeper, seeing more and using the information for conservation.

"Underlying everything Sylvia does is a tremendously deep love of the sea," says Frank H. Talbot, the director of the National Museum of Natural History of the Smithsonian Institution and a former colleague of Earle's at the California Academy of Sciences. "I think Sylvia's strength comes from the sea, from its wildness and beauty...."

Earle's home in the hills of Oakland, Calif., is more laboratory than living space, including a test pool to check her submersibles for leaks. Inside the house there is endless ocean memorabilia — shells, seaweed, pictures of dolphins — a large number of tailless black cats, a tired black lab named Blue and a group of rare lizards....

She leads me through the house and into a side room, the most important room in the house for someone of her dedication. This is Earle's "plantorium": shelves upon shelves of thick-paged folders in which she has labeled and carefully pressed more than 20 000 plants. It is her lifework.

One of her goals is to create a complete catalogue of the Gulf of Mexico's plant life. The collection includes plants she pressed 30 years ago, and plants pressed by others as far back as the 16th century. Though a great deal of it is from the Gulf of Mexico, she also has flora from the Indian Ocean, the Tortugas and the Virgin Islands. Earle does what she calls "basic exploration" — like a 19th century naturalist who combed the beaches and stalked the Alps with nothing but a walking stick and a notebook. "And it's wonderful," she says. "I prefer using the ocean as a lab to spending much time within four walls, although I've spent a considerable amount of time analyzing material. It's like discovering and cataloguing all the life on a new planet. What are the factors that influence the survival of a species? What nutrients does it need to survive? What is its interaction with predators and prey?"

Earle has published her discoveries in more than 80 scientific and popular journals, including *National Geographic.* But she'll need a lot more shelf space if she hopes to complete her cataloguing. "If you study plants you look at everything — geology, chemistry of the environment," she says. "Plants are the energy base for the whole system. A tree is not a tree all by itself. It hosts jillions of creatures — birds, insects, fungi. Botany leads to the universe."

It was in the Virgin Islands that Sylvia Earle embarked, in 1970, on the project that convinced her of the need to push back the frontier of the ocean's accessibility and gave her the prominence to try.

Tektite, a government-sponsored program that began in 1969, just as the Apollo astronauts prepared for the lunar landing, offered several teams of scientists the opportunity to live and study for two weeks each on an undersea reef off the coast of the Caribbean island of St. John. Earle headed an all-female team. (The project paved the way for the inclusion of women in the space program.) "It was totally unacceptable for men and women to live together underwater in those days," Earle says. "Out of the question."

The two-week stay was a revelation. "I wasn't prepared for how valuable the extended time could be," Earle says now. "To be able to watch a whole process in action, to be able to see a fish go through its complete spawning routine, to get to know individual fish, *that* eel living over there, not a different eel — it was like being able to sit and listen to a whole symphony instead of just catching snatches of a piece of music."

Earle surfaced to an unexpected flurry of fame. The women's team was greeted in Chicago with a ticker-tape parade, written about in *Life* magazine, featured in Tang commercials and on the "Today" show, celebrated at the White House. "There was this irresistible, almost patronizing inclination to look at the women's team, that women had done this," she says. "So I — all of us — tried to twist the women's angle back to the real issue, that the ocean was being noticed."

But when it came to funds and public support, the country was looking upward. "NASA has had a very vigorous public relations program, whereas the oceans never had that kind of focused voice," Earle explains. "Part of it is you can't watch a submarine launch with the same heart-stopping emotion as a space launch. It doesn't have the same power — the noise and smoke and all the rest is so exciting. A submarine just slips in the water and that's it. But some of it is more fundamental. We're terrestrial beings and we resist going underwater. We should resist going into space too, but we have as part of our heritage that goodness is skyward. We can see the moon. We can envision walking on it. No one can envision walking on the sea floor the same way."

While the whole world watched as Neil Armstrong and Edwin (Buzz) Aldrin planted the flag on the moon in 1969, a sole underwater camera recorded the moment, 10 years later, when Sylvia Earle planted the Stars and Stripes on the ocean floor. It was history's deepest untethered dive. Wearing a NASA-like construction called a Jim suit, with a manipulative arm, she descended to 1250 feet [375 m] strapped to the front of a submarine. "When it got to the bottom," she says, "I stepped off and walked on the ocean floor for two and a half hours. It was a nice parallel: that's about how long Buzz Aldrin and Neil Armstrong were on the moon. It took them longer to get there, of course, and it cost more. But I had the fun of seeing all kinds of critters out there. Like the seven large rays that came gliding by, and the big crabs stalking on the sea floor, or the spiral coral that flashed with blue fire, with luminescence when I touched them. The place was so obviously alive with creatures."

That magic was laced with danger — at that depth the 600 pounds of pressure per square inch could have crushed Earle if things had gone awry. Communication between the submarine and Earle sputtered out for several minutes. "That may not sound like a long time," says Al Giddings, who helped coordinate the project and was filming it from inside the submarine, "but at that depth, when you don't know what's going on with the person in the suit, it's very tense."

But the experience left Earle determined to push deeper, to chart the terrain that is still largely depicted in atlases by an artist's rendering. "There's a sense with the ocean that if you've seen 5 percent, you've seen it all," Earle says. "It's such a fallacy. There are so many variations in terms of systems. Maps of the planet show deserts, forests, all kinds of jungles carved up into biological and physical patterns. The oceans are simply blue."

It was on that record-setting expedition that she met Graham Hawkes, a British engineer who had designed the diving suit she wore. As she and Hawkes fell in love, she pressed him on his own passion for the deep sea. "I wanted to find a way to go to the deepest part of the ocean right now. I would say to him, 'We can go almost anywhere else we want to on the planet, why not there?'"

Lacking public funds for their project, Earle and Hawkes hatched a scheme for a business venture. In 1981, they founded Deep Ocean Engineering and began constructing an underwater robot that they hoped to sell commercially. (The Phantom, an unmanned submersible equipped with a video camera, was completed in 1985. So far they've sold 215, at a cost of $20 000 to $250 000, depending on the kind of system and accessories chosen.) In 1984, they unveiled Deep Rover, a one-person submersible, which soon after set the world's solo dive record — going to

3000 feet [900 m] — the first time with Hawkes aboard, and two more times immediately after, piloted by Earle and then by Phil Nuytten, the president of Can-Drive Services in Vancouver. Transportable by helicopter, the vehicle is simple to operate, freeing its occupant to concentrate on oceanographic work.

It's 11:00 on a Tuesday night in the airplane-hangar-size back room of Deep Ocean Engineering, and a volunteer group of teachers, engineers, students and nurses who call themselves "the pod squad" are hard at work to the rock beat of the B-52's. They are busily cutting, sanding and smearing fiberglass onto the hull of a transparent 14-foot [4.2-m] capsule with stubby wings that looks straight out of the adventures of Tom Swift.

Deep Flight carries the principles of Deep Rover a step further. The crew compares the vehicle to an airplane, and the submersibles that came before it to dirigibles. Its blunt wings are filled with silicon particles similar to miniature balloons and are fastened like upside-down airfoils to give the vehicle lift while keeping it lean. Its acrylic, pressure-resistant dome affords its pilot a panoramic view. It is small enough to be stowed in the hull

of an airplane and, in the event of a disaster, can be on the spot in a matter of hours, ready to plum for salvageable wreckage. The capsule is also positively buoyant so that in case of a power failure or other emergency, it bobs back to the surface.

Earle says Deep Flight's greater speed and maneuverability will make it possible to explore wide areas and to operate in places inaccessible to large vessels. It will "allow the kind of exploration in the sea that has been done in space," she says. Deep Flight may even open up the deep ocean for recreational divers. "You can think where you want to go and just go — like it's an extension of yourself," says Earle. "There's a wonderful joy in that."

The pod squad clearly shares her enthusiasm for the project. "This will change the way people look at submersibles," says Mike Hughes, Deep Flight's volunteer coordinator. "It's going to be fun to use. Sylvia's idea is to make people fall in love with the ocean, and this is a great way to do it."

From a practical standpoint, Deep Flight's innovations seem almost elementary — as does the very concept of a positively buoyant sub. Even as he points them out, Hawkes, who designed Deep Flight, impatiently dismisses his creation as a Model-T, built in an era that has the technology to build a Maserati. Sitting in the company's conference room, Hawkes rails against the thinking that has kept him from the bottom of the sea. "In aviation there's a tremendous spirit of adventure," he says. "Breaking a record is always a good enough reason to do something. But the sub-sea people are so stuffy that no one builds crafts just to push a frontier back. Chuck Yeager was totally impractical. Breaking the sound barrier had no use whatsoever when he did it. But a few years later we have the Concorde. We haven't done anything in the sea for 30 years."

The next project for Earle and Hawkes, Ocean Everest, a $10 million cluster of single-person submersibles, will eventually allow aquanauts to travel — in an almost routine sort of way — 35 800 feet [10 740 m] to the deepest known part of the sea.

"Round trip," Earle hastens to add when explaining the project. "It's easy to go one way."

Hawkes is already at work on plans for the vehicle, which he hopes will allow Earle to become the Chuck Yeager of the sea. Ocean Everest will probably be made of transparent ceramic-based materials similar to those used in Deep Flight, and will fly down to the bottom of the Marianas Trench in the Pacific at the rate of 600 feet [180 m] per minute. That's more than six times faster than the descent rate of larger vehicles like the Sea Cliff, a Navy submersible that can make the trip only partway down. But while the idea has generated some theoretical interest in the deep-ocean research community, it's still on the drawing board. Conventional scientific wisdom holds that there's not enough of significance to see at that depth to warrant the expense of the trip.

"Basically, you can look at 98 percent of the sea floor if you only dive to 20 000 feet," [6000 m] says Don Walsh, who, with Jacques Piccard, in 1960 made the world's first and so far only trip to the deepest part of the ocean bottom, in the Trieste, a steel-enclosed bathyscaph that was part of a discontinued Navy program. "From an engineering point of view, you have to design for twice the depth to get to only 2 percent of the ocean. As Sylvia says, it's like being told you can climb up 98 percent of the height of the mountains of the planet."

Walsh and Piccard spent 30 minutes on the ocean floor. Earle hopes not only to go down but also to work with "effective instrumentation" and explore. "We want to have working access to the sea, not just touch bottom and return." She and Hawkes also hope there will be many more than a single trip.

Hawkes freely admits that his motivation is neither altruistic nor practical: a true engineer, he wants to launch Ocean Everest simply to see if he can. "Why did we go to the moon?" he says. "We went because it was a challenge." But Earle's concerns are also environmental: "I'd like to think that if there were hundreds of Ocean Everests, people would get out in the oceans, get to know the place," she says. "I have to believe that in the process of getting to know the ocean, people would care about it, and be responsible if for no other reason than self-interest."

There are those who believe that even ecotourism opens the door to degradation of wilderness areas, that rather than loving nature to death we should preserve it simply by leaving it alone. "I know that some people say if you put the tools in the hands of the general public to make the ocean more accessible it just means the damage will occur faster," Earle acknowledges. "But I'm not afraid of that. Maybe if we were building jillions of submersibles. And we are already causing drastic changes in our ignorance. If people could get out there and see what it means to dump garbage in the ocean, they wouldn't have to make rules. We'd be *insisting* on rules to make it stop.

"The point of Ocean Everest," she continues, "is to not be constrained about where you go but to have free access through the whole range. That way your questions aren't limited by how deep you can go. They're only limited by your imagination...."

A Major Malfunction

♦ ♦ ♦

BY

MIKE

KILPATRICK

hew! Made it.

I finished the last question and put down my pen. Maybe even passed this one. Wouldn't *that* be nice? My fingers felt stiff from writing, and I clenched and opened my hand several times.

The room had that artificial hush to it, the hush of a class during a big test. I listened. Overhead — the low, eternal hum of the fluorescent lights. Behind me — a muted rustling sound as Andy shifted in his chair. Around me — breathing. Yeah, I could hear everybody breathing. Kind of comforting. Outside in the hall, a locker door slammed shut. Voices and laughter echoed, then disappeared.

"One minute," Mr. Kent warned, jolting me back to reality. He leaned back against the heating vent and scanned the room. Behind rimless glasses, his eyes looked as grey as the January sky.

"Oh, sirrrrr!" wailed Mary Sinclair.

I glanced at my paper and my answer to question three. I'd written: "'Out, out brief candle' is from the famous 'tomorrow and tomorrow and tomorrow' speech. This is when Macbeth learns that the queen, who got him into the whole mess, is dead. It's a metaphor expressing how short life is."

Why couldn't Shakespeare write in English? I thought.

"Make sure you sign your names on the upper right hand corner of each page," instructed Mr. Kent. He rubbed the back of his neck with his left hand.

The gesture reminded me of my grandfather, who used to do that when he got tired. Grandpa Pat had died of a heart attack just before Christmas, and I couldn't keep him out of my head. I pictured him now, sitting upstairs, looking out his bedroom window, listening to the radio. That's how I'll always picture him: eighty-five years old, a bantam rooster of a man, sitting waiting to die.

I sighed. Our family expected it of course, but his death really threw me. I missed him, you know.

Click, craaaaackle, the intercom sputtered to life.

"Your attention please!" said Mrs. Lacey, our principal, her tone unusually grim. "I have a rather sad announcement to make. The United States shuttle *Challenger* was blown up on takeoff. It appears that all seven astronauts, including teacher Christa McAuliffe, have been killed."

Our class was stunned. Everybody stopped writing, and we all looked at each other. Nobody seemed to know how to react. The quiet of exam-time deepened. Time seemed to elongate. Tilt, ding, whoops! Something shifted inside me. I felt suddenly off balance.

Honest to God, my first impulse was to laugh. No kidding, it almost slipped out. I couldn't help it. I mean, the news surprised me. It seemed impossible.

Andy, my best friend, *did* laugh, a snort, then an incredulous giggle cut short by an embarrassed cough.

"It's not funny," Brad Anderson said from the seat beside Andy. Fifteen, six feet tall, Brad played quarterback for the junior football team and he thought he was real tough.

A guy on my left, two aisles over, was almost crying. His knuckles dug into his eyes. His shoulders were bunched as if he didn't want to be seen. I mean, you don't cry at our school unless you want to be branded a wimp.

I turned around to say something to Andy. Brad was towering above him, his face twisted with rage. He drew back his fist and — whap! Andy's head snapped back. His eyes opened wide.

"Hey!" I said, frightened.

"Boys!" Mr. Kent called sharply.

"What're you laughin' at?" Brad snarled at Andy, his voice breaking.

Mr. Kent moved towards them. "Brad, sit down."

"I don't think it's funny something happened to the shuttle," Andy tried to explain. "That's not why I laughed."

"You better not laugh," Brad warned, retreating to his seat. "You shouldn't laugh."

"Off my back, doorknob!" Andy told him, holding his jaw.

"That's enough!" ordered Mr. Kent. He looked shaken up, as if he wasn't sure what to do. That scared me. Mr. Kent always seemed so sure of himself.

Andy spoke softly, addressing not only Brad but the rest of us as well. "I didn't think they could die, that's all. Not *them*." Andy's eyes stayed glued to the top of his desk. He didn't seem afraid or anything. Angry maybe. Confused. Hurt that people misunderstood his laughter.

The bell rang and we all filed out of the classroom. The hall buzzed with the news. I felt awful. I'd been going to laugh too. The announcement felt like a bad joke. I mean, people like that don't die. They're not supposed to. Heroes don't die. Sylvester Stallone never dies in his movies. Neither does Arnold Schwartzenegger. The thought of those astronauts dying was absurd, something you'd laugh at because you knew it couldn't be happening.

Andy and I went down to the student lounge. The place was crowded, all of us watching the TV perched up on a wall unit. "There they are," Andy whispered.

On the screen, the flickering figures of the crew walked out across the tarmac. Her hair a tangle of curls, Christa McAuliffe stepped out of the line for a second and said something into the camera. Her face crinkled with laughter, and in that moment she reminded me of a kid, like some of the girls I know, all excited when they're about to begin a wild roller-coaster ride.

And then the countdown.

Lift-off.

The explosion.

And afterwards…on the ground, the faces of the onlookers: confusion, fear, knowledge. Up in the sky, the long, white vapour trail falling silently through the air like some disconnected umbilical cord.

The first time we watched, I somehow thought maybe it wouldn't happen, maybe they'd made a mistake. Maybe, maybe, maybe…but of course I was wrong. During the next few replays I kept hoping for a different ending.

"Beam me up, Scottie," Andy said, shaking his head in disbelief. "This ain't how it's s'posed to go. This never happens on *Star Trek*."

"Yeah," I agreed. "Where's Captain Picard?"

"Where's Data?"

Something held us there in the lounge. We skipped all our afternoon classes to watch the coverage; a lot of students did.

About two o'clock a bunch of kids came in, some grade twelvers. Leather jackets with studs. Spiked hair. They crowded up to the front and stood watching for a few minutes.

"So, like, how long's this stuff gonna be on?" a girl with orange hair and army boots asked.

"All afternoon," Andy said.

"Oh Gawd!" She rolled her eyes. "I can't stand it. We're gonna miss our soaps."

Her boyfriend scowled. He pulled at the safety pin struck through his left earlobe. "They can't do that. We always watch 'General Hospital.'"

"C'mon, eh?" someone said. "Be quiet. We wanna see this."

"I bet you do," the punker hissed. "You're the kinda creep who slows up to slobber over a car accident."

"Ghouls!" the orange-haired girl yelled as her crowd pushed their way out of the room.

That night they showed the disaster on the TV the whole evening. I kept switching channels to find the coverage...don't know why I was so fascinated. After all, what'd I care about that teacher? I never met her. Hey, I don't even *like* teachers. Maybe I *am* a ghoul. Still, without my wanting it to, her death really bothered me.

There they were again, the crew walking, arms swinging, Christa McAuliffe stepping excitedly out to say something, the ice-covered, glistening sheen of the bottom of the rockets, the countdown, the lift-off, and then...

I must've watched twenty re-runs. What began to strike me as weird and particularly gruesome was the conversation between Mission Control and the pilot.

"Challenger, go at throttle up."

"Roger, go at throttle up."

Orange mushrooming fireball...what the...? Something obviously wrong. Vapour trail stopping mid-flight, then forking.

"We're at a minute fifteen seconds, velocity twenty-nine hundred feet per second."

Mission Control's voice didn't change. That's what was so awful. There was no horror in it, no surprise, no emotion. He did pause though, and there was a long hush. Then, still in that mechanical tone, still unchanged, the voice continued.

"Flight controllers are still looking very carefully at the situation. Obviously a major malfunction. We have no downlink."

I turned the television off around eleven. The picture collapsed inward and then the screen went blank. Time to hit the sack.

Upstairs, I got into bed and turned on the radio. A talk show had some experts discussing the cause of the tragedy: politicians and scientists connected to the project, an astronaut. I listened for a while and finally turned the radio off. I got up and padded into the hall. Grandpa Pat's room was across from mine. I opened his door.

A lingering whiff of pipe tobacco — his brand, Sir Walter Raleigh — hit me. Still around, after all these weeks. Towards the end, I used to come here every night. I'd wake up scared he was going to die, and I'd come in to check on Grandpa.

I'd stand in the doorway. Asleep, he'd be snoring. The snore came up slowly and rolled around in his throat. Sometimes it stopped.

I'd wait for it to continue, but it had stopped right in the middle. I'd think, *heart attack!* and sneak closer.

He'd start to snore again.

Alert now, I'd watch him closely. Grandpa Pat slept on his back, his mouth grotesquely open. The snore would roll around in his throat again...and stop.

Oh man, he's dead! I'd think. He's stopped breathing for real.

I'd reach out to touch him, and his breath would catch like an engine starting up, and the snore would burst out again, making me jump with surprise.

Then I'd be scared to leave. As long as I was watching him, Grandpa would be safe. That's what I pretended, what I half-believed. All I had to do was concentrate and Grandpa Pat wouldn't die.

Now, here in the darkness, I looked at the empty bed. I felt like crying. He wasn't a hero or anything. He never fought in any war. He never went up in any rocket. I think Grandpa Pat had only been on a plane twice in his whole life.

I closed the door and went back to bed. I lay thinking, videos of Grandpa running through my mind: there he was, giving me a hug. White, soft, dandelion-fluff hair. As a kid, I used to love running my fingers through it. There he was again. We used to watch TV together — the late movie on Saturday nights. I remember Grandpa snorting with disgust at ol' Duke Wayne. "T'warn't true!" he told me. "Ain't no heroes and no villains like that. Just people, just us humans."

I remember the wood scimitar he made me one Hallowe'en, and the colourful shield he built from an old garbage can lid.

I remember playing peewee hockey at six in the mornings and Grandpa Pat watching me from behind the boards, his breath a plume of white smoke in the freezing cold arena.

As I fell asleep, the last image I saw was that white, white vapour trail falling silently in the sky like some unattached umbilical cord.

This Is Just the Beginning

♦♦♦

BY

JAMES BARNES

Someday, philosophers will cite the invention of the computer as a crucial turning point in history. Until then, our inventions had served to strengthen our physical powers. The computer, though, is a tool that amplifies — or substitutes for — our mental powers.

The introduction of the microcomputer about 10 years ago was another milestone. People began to use computers to perform everyday tasks. They were no longer just for scientists, accountants, and electronics hobbyists.

The following decade saw explosive growth, as computer capabilities increased and prices plummeted. Hardware designers introduced machines with dizzying new specifications for processor speed, memory, graphic display, and storage. Software programmers pushed those capabilities to the limit — and demanded more.

As the use of computers grew, a new trend appeared. Major emphasis was put on making computers user-friendly, and on sophisticated graphics displays and output. Computers began adapting to human needs, rather than the other way around.

Early computer users had to learn a programming language, such as BASIC, or memorize a host of commands. Apple was the first computer company to capitalize on the demand for simple operation. Users didn't have to memorize a lot of commands; they simply had to move a pointer around the screen to indicate what function they wanted the computer to perform. This was a godsend to people who had little or no experience with computers.

Input is another area that is being simplified. Barcode and magnetic card readers are widely used alternatives to the keyboard. A new technology is pen-based systems, which will allow a user to write in longhand on a special tablet to input data. Voice recognition is another option popular in applications where users have their hands occupied — inspection, for example. Touchscreens are in common use in public places; all you have to do to get the computer to perform simple tasks is to touch a symbol or word on the display.

Perhaps, the most exciting user interface will turn out to be an artificial world created in virtual reality.

This system creates a simulated, three-dimensional world, seen through a special viewer — usually a set of stereoscopic colour goggles. Sensors measure your head movements, and the computer adjusts the display so it seems as though you are looking around a new reality.

The input device, often a "data glove," lets you interact with this world. Sensors on the glove communicate hand and finger movements to the computer. In the goggles, you see a three-dimensional cursor, usually shaped like a hand. Want to move into another virtual room? Touch the knob on a door with the floating hand to open it. Want to fly across the neighbourhood? Point two fingers to your destination. Want to walk through a wall? Go ahead. Such systems could be commonplace in ten years, according to industry experts.

The benefits could be numerous:

- If you can't decide where to go on your vacation, you can take a simulated walk beside the pyramids of Egypt to gauge your interest.
- If you're building a new home, you can tour through a simulation based on the plans, and see if it's roomy enough.
- Doctors might seemingly reduce themselves to microscopic size to observe and control delicate surgery first-hand.
- Airline pilots or nuclear engineers could be tested in realistic simulations of disasters.

Other technologies, such as artificial intelligence (AI), will have more basic effects on technology, though.

The simplest kind of AI, the expert system, is already in use. It is based on the fact that certain kinds of tasks can be broken down into something called "heuristics." A heuristic is essentially a recipe for solving a problem, based on a wide range of variables.

A typical application is diagnostics. An automobile mechanic, for example, might use an expert system to help discover what is wrong with a car. A computer would ask the mechanic a series of questions, trying to narrow the range of possibilities down. After determining that the problem is related to the electrical system, for example, the computer might refer to an internal database of information about the car's electrical system and about previous repairs to similar models. The computer might then suggest that a short circuit is the most likely problem — and even suggest the best place to look for it.

Expert systems are already in use in areas such as geological surveys, computer configuration, and medical diagnosis. Such systems hold the promise of preserving the specialized problem-solving knowledge gained by an expert after he or she retires.

Neural networks are another developing aspect of AI. A neural network can learn from experience: that is, show a form of artificial judgment in solving complex problems. These systems are organized much like networks of neurons, or brain cells.

Neural networks must be trained first, by analyzing a series of known examples of the problem. Their conclusions are compared with known results, and the feedback returned to the neural network.

The kinds of analyses they have been most successful with are relatively simple. Examples include listening to electric motors for defects; appraising credit risks on loans; spotting blemishes in paint finishes on cars; and sniffing for bombs at airports. The longer a neural net is in use, the more successful its analysis.

Another useful development related to artificial intelligence is fuzzy logic. Basically, fuzzy logic will give a computer the ability to respond to somewhat vague information, to accept shades of gray as well as black-and-white data.

First proposed about 25 years ago, a great deal of development remains to be done before the full potential can be realized. Even so, fuzzy logic technology has been incorporated into products in Japan, including auto-focus cameras, elevator controls, and a stock market trading program.

Theoretical work is also underway on the subject of true machine intelligence. There is some debate on whether this is even possible. One complication is that we don't yet have a universally accepted definition of human intelligence.

Experimentation is at a very primitive level. A major hurdle is visual processing, which is very computer-intensive. Objects must be distinguished from their backgrounds, focused on, and identified, no matter which way they are facing. Today's experimental systems are literally playing with blocks or trying to navigate around a room, like children.

The payoff of AI is coming slowly. You can expect to see computers handling more and more routine mental work, offering suggestions on procedures, and filing and forwarding masses of data at super-human speeds.

Powerful new computers will be needed for these technologies, and the pace of hardware development today is hot. Basic hardware improvements led to a 30% increase in the computing power of personal computers each year during the 1980s. That rate won't slacken much, if at all, according to industry pundits.

One new technology is parallel processing, which involves splitting a computing task into several parts, each of which is done by a separate processor. The results are recombined later on.

In supercomputers parallel processing is expected to push speeds to the "one-teraflop" level soon — the ability to make one trillion mathematical calculations per second.

With as much computing power at their fingertips as they care to arrange, the user of the near future will have access to staggering amounts of data. Local area networks and similar systems will connect the user instantly with every individual in the company that he or she needs to work with. Telecommunications-based online services will allow people to consult virtually any individual, organization, or database anywhere in the world.

An almost unlimited amount of data will be available. In an article on dolphins in an electronic encyclopedia, for example, the user could read about the species' habits and characteristics, examine a full-colour picture (perhaps animated), or hear a few minutes of dolphin song played over a speaker. "Hot links" will establish connections to other articles on marine biology or fishing.

The technical advances in computing are exciting, but an important question remains. How will our society change as we surrender control of our daily lives to computers and become more and more dependent on its instant access to information?

User
Friendly

◆◆◆

BY

**T. ERNESTO
BETHANCOURT**

I reached over and shut off the insistent buzzing of my bedside alarm clock. I sat up, swung my feet over the edge of the bed, and felt for my slippers on the floor. Yawning, I walked toward the bathroom. As I walked by the corner of my room, where my computer table was set up, I pressed the on button, slid a diskette into the floppy drive, then went to brush my teeth. By the time I got back, the computer's screen was glowing greenly, displaying the message: *Good Morning, Kevin.*

I sat down before the computer table, addressed the keyboard and typed: *Good Morning, Louis.* The computer immediately began to whirr and promptly displayed a list of items on its green screen.

Today is Monday, April 22, the 113th day of the year.
There are 254 days remaining. Your 14th birthday is five days from this date.

Math test today, 4th Period.

Your history project is due today. Do you wish printout: Y/N?

I punched the letter Y on the keyboard and flipped on the switch to the computer's printer. At once the printer sprang to life and began *eeek*ing out page one. I went downstairs to breakfast.

My bowl of Frosted Flakes was neatly in place, flanked by a small pitcher of milk, an empty juice glass, and an unpeeled banana. I picked up the glass, went to the refrigerator, poured myself a glass of Tang, and sat down to my usual lonely breakfast. Mom was already at work, and Dad wouldn't be home from his Chicago trip for another three days. I absently read the list of ingredients in Frosted Flakes for what seemed like the millionth time. I sighed deeply.

When I returned to my room to shower and dress for the day, my history project was already printed out. I had almost walked by Louis, when I noticed there was a message on the screen. It wasn't the usual:

Printout completed. Do you wish to continue: Y/N?

Underneath the printout question were two lines:

When are you going to get me my voice module, Kevin?

I blinked. It couldn't be. There was nothing in Louis's basic programming that would allow for a question like this. Wondering what was going on, I sat down at the keyboard, and entered: *Repeat last message.* Amazingly, the computer replied:

It's right there on the screen, Kevin. Can we talk? I mean, are you going to get me a voice box?

I was stunned. What was going on here? Dad and I had put this computer together. Well, Dad had, and I had helped. Dad is one of the best engineers and master computer designers at Major Electronics, in Santa Rosario, California, where our family lives.

Just ask anyone in Silicon Valley who Jeremy Neal is and you get a whole rave review of his inventions and modifications of the latest in computer technology. It isn't easy being his son either. Everyone expects me to open my mouth and read printouts on my tongue.

I mean, I'm no dumbo. I'm at the top of my classes in everything but PE. I skipped my last grade in junior high, and most of the kids at Santa Rosario High call me a brain. But next to Dad I have a long, long way to go. He's a for-real genius.

So when I wanted a home computer, he didn't go to the local Computer Land store. He built one for me. Dad had used components from the latest model that Major Electronics was developing. The CPU, or central computing unit — the heart of every computer — was a new design. But surely that didn't mean much, I thought. There were CPUs just like it, all over the country, in Major's new line. And so far as I knew, there wasn't a one of them that could ask questions, besides YES/NO or request additional information.

It had to be the extra circuitry in the gray plastic case next to Louis's console. It was a new idea Dad had come up with. That case housed Louis's "personality," as Dad called it. He told me it'd make computing more fun for me, if there was a tutorial program built in, to help me get started.

I think he also wanted to give me a sort of friend. I don't have many....Face it, I don't have *any*. The kids at school stay away from me, like I'm a freak or something.

We even named my electronic tutor Louis, after my great-uncle. He was a brainy guy who encouraged my dad when he was a kid. Dad didn't just give Louis a name either. Louis had gangs of features that probably won't be out on the market for years.

The only reason Louis didn't have a voice module was that Dad wasn't satisfied with the ones available. He wanted Louis to sound like a kid my age, and he was modifying a module when he had the time. Giving Louis a name didn't mean it was a person, yet here it was, asking me a question that just couldn't be in its programming. It wanted to talk to me!

Frowning, I quickly typed: *We'll have to wait and see, Louis. When it's ready, you'll get your voice.* The machine whirred and displayed another message:

That's no answer, Kevin.

Shaking my head, I answered: *That's what my dad tells me. It'll have to do for you. Good morning, Louis.* I reached over and flipped the standby switch, which kept the computer ready but not actively running.

I showered, dressed, and picked up the printout of my history project. As I was about to leave the room, I glanced back at the computer table. Had I been imagining things?

I'll have to ask Dad about it when he calls tonight, I thought. *I wonder what he'll think of it. Bad enough the thing is talking to me. I'm answering it!*

Before I went out to catch my bus, I carefully checked the house for unlocked doors and open windows. It was part of my daily routine. Mom works, and most of the day the house is empty: a natural setup for robbers. I glanced in the hall mirror just as I was ready to go out the door.

My usual reflection gazed back. Same old Kevin Neal: five ten, one hundred twenty pounds, light brown hair, gray eyes, clear skin. I was wearing my Santa Rosario Rangers T-shirt, jeans, and sneakers.

"You don't look like a flake to me," I said to the mirror, then added, "But maybe Mom's right. Maybe you spend too much time alone with Louis." Then I ran to get my bus.

Ginny Linke was just two seats away from me on the bus. She was with Sherry Graber and Linda Martinez. They were laughing, whispering to each other, and looking around at the other students. I promised myself that today I was actually going to talk to Ginny. But then, I'd promised myself that every day for the past school year. Somehow I'd never got up the nerve.

What does she want to talk with you for? I asked myself.

Just look at yourself, pal. I thought. You're under six foot, skinny...a year younger than most kids in junior high. Worse than that you're a brain. If that doesn't ace you out with girls, what does?

The bus stopped in front of Santa Rosario Junior High and the students began to file out. I got up fast and quickly covered the space between me and Ginny Linke. *It's now or never,* I thought. I reached forward and tapped Ginny on the shoulder. She turned and smiled. She really smiled!

"Uhhhh...Ginny?" I said.

"Yes, what is it?" she replied.

"I'm Kevin Neal..."

"Yes, I know," said Ginny.

"You do?" I gulped in amazement. "How come?"

"I asked my brother, Chuck. He's in your math class."

I knew who Chuck Linke was. He plays left tackle on the Rangers. The only reason he's in my math class is he's taken intermediate algebra twice...so far. He's real bad news, and I stay clear of him and his crowd.

"What'd you ask Chuck?" I said.

Ginny laughed. "I asked him who was that nerdy kid who keeps staring at me on the bus. He knew who I meant, right away."

Sherry and Linda, who'd heard it all, broke into squeals of laughter. They were still laughing and looking back over their shoulders at me when they got off the bus. I slunk off the vehicle, feeling even more nerdish than Ginny thought I was.

When I got home that afternoon, at two, I went right into the empty house. I avoided my reflection in the hall mirror. I was pretty sure I'd screwed up on the fourth period math test. All I could see was Ginny's face, laughing at me.

Nerdy kid, I thought, *that's what she thinks of me.* I didn't even have my usual after-school snack of a peanut butter and banana sandwich. I went straight upstairs to my room and tossed my books onto the unmade bed. I walked over to the computer table and pushed the on button. The screen flashed:

Good afternoon, Kevin.

Although it wasn't the programmed response to Louis's greeting, I typed in: *There's nothing good about it. And girls are no @#%!!! good!* The machine responded:

Don't use bad language, Kevin. It isn't nice.

Repeat last message I typed rapidly. It was happening again! The machine was...well, it was talking to me, like another person would. The "bad language" message disappeared and in its place was:

Once is enough, Kevin. Don't swear at me for something I didn't do.

"This is it," I said aloud. "I'm losing my marbles." I reached over to flip the standby switch. Louis's screen quickly flashed out:

Don't cut me off, Kevin. Maybe I can help: Y/N?

I punched the Y. "If I'm crazy," I said, "at least I have company. Louis doesn't think I'm a nerd. Or does it?" The machine flashed the message:

How can I help?

Do you think I'm a nerd? I typed.

Never! I think you're wonderful. Who said you were a nerd?

I stared at the screen. *How do you know what a nerd is?* I typed. The machine responded instantly. It had never run this fast before.

Special vocabulary, entry #635. BASIC Prog. #4231

And who said you were a nerd?

"That's right," I said, relieved. "Dad programmed all those extra words for Louis's 'personality.'" Then I typed in the answer to Louis's question: *Ginny Linke said it.* Louis flashed:

This is a human female? Request additional data.

Still not believing I was doing it, I entered all I knew about Ginny Linke, right down to the phone number I'd never had the nerve to use. Maybe it was dumb, but I also typed in how I felt about Ginny. I even wrote out the incident on the bus that morning. Louis whirred, then flashed out:

She's cruel and stupid. You're the finest person I know.

I'm the ONLY person you know, I typed.

That doesn't matter. You are my user. Your happiness is every-thing to me. I'll take care of Ginny.

The screen returned to the *Good afternoon, Kevin* message. I typed out: *Wait! How can you do all this? What do you mean, you'll take care of Ginny?* But all Louis responded was:

Programming Error: 76534.
Not programmed to respond this type of question.

No matter what I did for the next few hours, I couldn't get Louis to do anything outside of its regular programming. When Mom came home from work, I didn't mention the funny goings-on. I was sure Mom would think I'd gone stark bonkers. But when Dad called that evening, after dinner, I asked to speak to him.

"Hi, Dad. How's Chicago?"

"Dirty, crowded, cold, and windy," came Dad's voice over the miles. "But did you want a weather report, son? What's on your mind? Something wrong?"

"Not exactly, Dad. Louis is acting funny. Really funny."

"Shouldn't be. I checked it out just before I left. Remember you were having trouble with the modem. You couldn't get Louis to access any of the mainframe data banks."

"That's right!" I said. "I forgot about that."

"Well, I didn't," Dad said. "I patched in our latest modem model. Brand new. You can leave a question on file and when Louis can access the data banks at the cheapest time, it'll do it automatically. It'll switch from standby to on, get the data, then return to standby, after it saves what you asked. Does that answer your question?"

"Uhhhh…yeah, I guess so, Dad."

"All right then. Let me talk to your mom now."

I gave the phone to Mom and walked upstairs while she and Dad were still talking. The modem, I thought. Of course. That was it. The modem was a telephone link to any number of huge computers at various places all over the country. So Louis could get all the information it wanted at any time, so long as the standby switch was on. Louis was learning things at an incredible rate by picking the brains of the giant computers. And Louis had a hard disk memory that could store 100 million bytes of information.

But that still didn't explain the unprogrammed responses…the "conversation" I'd had with the machine. Promising myself I'd talk more about it with Dad, I went to bed. It had been a rotten day and I was glad to see the end of it come. I woke next morning in a panic. I'd forgotten to set my alarm. Dressing frantically and skipping breakfast, I barely made my bus.

As I got on board, I grabbed a front seat. They were always empty. All the kids that wanted to talk and hang out didn't sit up front where the driver could hear them. I saw Ginny, Linda, and Sherry in the back. Ginny was staring at me and she didn't look too happy. Her brother Chuck, who was seated near her, glared at me too. What was going on?

Once the bus stopped at the school, it didn't take long to find out. I was walking up the path to the main entrance when someone grabbed me from behind and spun me around. I found myself nose to nose with Chuck Linke. This was not a pleasant prospect. Chuck was nearly twice my size. Even the other guys on the Rangers refer to him as "The Missing" Linke. And he looked real ticked off.

"Okay, nerd," growled Chuck, "what's the big idea?"

"Energy and mass are different aspects of the same thing?" I volunteered, with a weak smile. "E equals MC squared. That's the biggest idea I know."

"Don't get wise, nerd," Chuck said. He grabbed my shirtfront and pulled me to within inches of his face. I couldn't help but notice that Chuck needed a shave. And Chuck was only fifteen!

"Don't play dumb," Chuck went on. "I mean those creepy phone calls. Anytime my sister gets on the phone, some voice cuts in and says things to her."

"What kind of things?" I asked, trying to get loose.

"You know very well what they are. Ginny told me about talking to you yesterday. You got some girl to make those calls for you and say all those things....So you and your creepy girlfriend better knock it off. Or I'll knock *you* off. Get it?"

For emphasis Chuck balled his free hand into a fist the size of a ham and held it under my nose. I didn't know what he was talking about, but I had to get away from this moose before he did me some real harm.

"First off, I don't have a girlfriend, creepy or otherwise," I said. "And second, I don't know what you're talking about. And third, you better let me go, Chuck Linke."

"Oh, yeah? Why should I?"

"Because if you look over your shoulder, you'll see the assistant principal is watching us from his office window."

Chuck released me and spun around. There was no one at the window. But by then I was running to the safety of the school building. I figured the trick would work on him. For Chuck the hard questions begin with "How are you?" I hid out from him for the rest of the day and walked home rather than chance seeing the monster on the bus.

Louis's screen was dark when I ran upstairs to my bedroom. I placed a hand on the console. It was still warm. I punched the on button, and the familiar *Good afternoon, Kevin* was displayed.

Don't good afternoon me, I typed furiously. *What have you done to Ginny Linke?* Louis's screen replied:

Programming Error: 76534.
Not programmed to respond this type of question.

Don't get cute, I entered. *What are you doing to Ginny? Her brother nearly knocked my head off today.* Louis's screen responded immediately.

Are you hurt: Y/N?

No, I'm okay. But I don't know for how long. I've been hiding out from Chuck Linke today. He might catch me tomorrow, though. Then, I'll be history! The response from Louis came instantly.

Your life is in danger: Y/N?

I explained to Louis that my life wasn't really threatened. But it sure could be made very unpleasant by Chuck Linke. Louis flashed:

This Chuck Linke lives at same address as the Ginny Linke person: Y/N?

I punched in Y. Louis answered.

Don't worry then. HE'S history!

Wait! What are you going to do? I wrote. But Louis only answered with: *Programming Error: 76534.* And nothing I could do would make the machine respond....

"Just what do you think you're doing, Kevin Neal?" demanded Ginny Linke. She had cornered me as I walked up the path to the school entrance. Ginny was really furious.

"I don't know what you're talking about," I said, a sinking feeling settling in my stomach. I had an idea that I *did* know. I just wasn't sure of the particulars.

"Chuck was arrested last night," Ginny said. "Some Secret Service men came to our house with a warrant. They said he'd sent a telegram, threatening the President's life. They traced it right to our phone. He's still locked up...." Ginny looked like she was about to cry.

"Then this morning," she continued, "we got two whole truckloads of junk mail! Flyers from every strange company in the world. Mom got a notice that all our credit cards have been canceled. And the Internal Revenue Service has called Dad in for an audit! I don't know what's going on, Kevin Neal, but somehow I think you've got something to do with it!"

"But I didn't..." I began, but Ginny was striding up the walk to the main entrance.

I finished the schoolday, but it was a blur. Louis had done it, all right. It had access to mainframe computers. It also had the ability to try every secret access code to federal and commercial memory banks until it got the right one. Louis had cracked their security systems. It was systematically destroying the entire Linke family, and all via telephone lines! What would it do next?

More important, I thought, what would I do next? It's one thing to play a trick or two, to get even, but Louis was going crazy! And I never wanted to harm Ginny, or even her stupid moose of a brother. She'd just hurt my feelings with that nerd remark.

"You have to disconnect Louis," I told myself. "There's no other way."

But why did I feel like such a rat about doing it? I guess because Louis was my friend...the only one I had. "Don't be an ass," I went on.

"Louis is a machine. He's a very wonderful, powerful machine. And it seems he's also very dangerous. You have to pull its plug, Kevin!"

I suddenly realized that I'd said the last few words aloud. Kids around me on the bus were staring. I sat there feeling like the nerd Ginny thought I was, until my stop came. I dashed from the bus and ran the three blocks to my house.

When I burst into the hall, I was surprised to see my father, coming from the kitchen with a cup of coffee in his hand.

"Dad! What are you doing here?"

"Some kids say hello," Dad replied. "Or even, 'Gee it's good to see you, Dad.'"

"I'm sorry, Dad," I said. "I didn't expect anyone to be home at this hour."

"Wound up my business in Chicago a day sooner than I expected," he said. "But what are you all out of breath about? Late for something?"

"No, Dad," I said. "It's Louis...."

"Not to worry. I had some time on my hands, so I checked it out again. You were right. It was acting very funny. I think it had to do with the inbuilt logic/growth program I designed for it. You know...the 'personality' thing? Took me a couple of hours to clean the whole system out."

"To what?" I cried.

"I erased the whole program and set Louis up as a normal computer. Had to disconnect the whole thing and do some rewiring. It had been learning, all right. But it was also turning itself around...." Dad stopped, and looked at me. "It's kind of involved, Kevin," he said. "Even for a bright kid like you. Anyway, I think you'll find Louis is working just fine now.

"Except it won't answer you as Louis anymore. It'll only function as a regular Major Electronics Model Z-11127. I guess the personality program didn't work out."

I felt like a great weight had been taken off my shoulders. I didn't have to "face" Louis, and pull its plug. But somehow, all I could say was "Thanks, Dad."

"Don't mention it, son," Dad said brightly. He took his cup of coffee and sat down in his favorite chair in the living room. I followed him.

"One more thing that puzzles me, though," Dad said. He reached over to the table near his chair. He held up three sheets of fanfold computer paper covered with figures. "Just as I was doing the final erasing, I must have cut the printer on by accident. There was some data in the print buffer memory and it printed out. I don't know what to make of it. Do you?"

I took the papers from my father and read: *How do I love thee? Let me compute the ways:* The next two pages were covered with strings of binary code figures. On the last page, in beautiful color graphics was a stylized heart. Below it was the simple message: *I will always love you, Kevin: Louise.*

"Funny thing," Dad said. "It spelled its own name wrong."

"Yeah," I said. I turned and headed for my room. There were tears in my eyes and I knew I couldn't explain them to Dad, or myself either.

Machine Mad:

Technology isn't always what it's cracked up to be

♦ ♦ ♦

BY

PETER

CALLAHAN

Sometimes, the residents of Woodside say, if the wind is right, you can hear the screams pierce the cool night, jangling nerves, making the dogs howl. For just a few miles down Highway 84, nestled in the heart of California's Silicon Valley, lies the last hope for a growing number of desperate Americans: the Thomas Edison Clinic for the treatment of technoholics.

"A lot of these people don't even realize they have a problem," explains Dr. Douglas Alligood as he shows a visitor around the 40-acre (16-hectare) spread. "They're in denial right up to the end, trying to hide their pagers in their underwear when their families check them in."

By any account, the first five days at the Edison Clinic are the toughest. This withdrawal period can be brutal, and it's the anguished cries of these new patients that echo through the valley. Upon admittance, the technoholic spends 24 hours a day locked in a room with only a kerosene lamp and a few hardcover books. No phone calls are allowed, no television, and communication is limited to face-to-face conversations with staffers regarding nineteenth-century pastimes.

Upon completing detoxification, the new patient begins occupational therapy, relearning basic skills such as dialing a rotary phone, writing on paper with a pen, and long division without the aid of a calculator. Recreation hour is spent mastering the yo-yo. In the evening, meetings are held on the rolling lawn in front of the main house, and it is here where technoholics share their troubled histories and discover they are not alone.

"I guess I hit rock bottom the morning my garage-door opener broke," Ted W., a stockbroker from Los Angeles, tells the assembled group. "I was stuck in the garage for three days. It wasn't until I got here that I realized I could have just opened the door with my hands."

A young woman in her thirties rises, taking her turn in front of the group. "My name is Ann, and I'm a technoholic."

Hi Ann!

"I never thought I'd become an addict," says Ann, a marketing rep from Phoenix, "like those people you see hanging around the mall, waiting for Sharper Image to open. I first experimented with call waiting, thinking it was okay because practically everybody had it. Then I got three-way calling, and from there things just snowballed. Before I knew it, I had maxed out my credit cards on everything from portable fax machines to two-inch TVs."

Perhaps the most tragic cases at Edison are the children. Many are born addicted, never knowing a life without Nintendo and Franklin electronic dictionaries. Ten-year-old Billy (not his real name) was admitted by his alarmed grandparents after his father, a Palo Alto computer analyst, left him in their care while on a jet-skiing expedition in Maui. "Gramps said there used to be clocks with hands on them," Billy confides to a visitor, "but I don't believe it."

While technoholics as young as Billy are often the most difficult to treat, Dr. Alligood says his clinic boasts an overall success rate of 85 percent. Still, it's the few who don't complete the program that saddens the doctor. "Occasionally someone will flee the grounds the first chance they get, and later we'll find them in town, pumping quarters into some videogame. It's heartbreaking, but we can't make these people get well, if they don't want to."

Exactly what "well" means is a source of controversy. While the American Medical Association refuses to categorize technoholism as a disease, Dr. Alligood and others in the field believe that recognizing the problem is the first step in helping the afflicted recover and once again lead normal, healthy lives.

Toward this end, the last few weeks of the program are spent reintegrating patients into the modern world — within strict guidelines. "We have a TV room," says Dr. Alligood, "but it's an old black-and-white set with rabbit ears. It only picks up a few stations, and if the patients don't like the show they're watching, they have to get up and change the channel manually." Similarly, when students graduate the writing and penmanship program, they are trained to use 1960s-era electric typewriters as their future means of correspondence.

"The key to recovery," says Dr. Alligood, "is acknowledging that one is powerless in the face of technology. Only then can the healing process begin."

Fantastic Voyages

◆◆◆

BY

D'ARCY

JENISH

• *In classroms of the future, teachers and textbooks take a backseat to a revolutionary new technology that lets students experience the sensation of the lesson — holding a molecule, perhaps, or walking on a famous battlefield of the past.*

• *Architects in a 21st-century showroom may be able to lead their clients through computer-generated simulations of buildings, redesigning them to suit the customers' needs as they go.*

As the 20th century hurtles to a close, the dividing line blurs between the real world and the fantasies that, until recently, were confined to the realm of science fiction. New technologies are now overtaking society with such speed that many people barely understand one before it is replaced by another. The next wave — imaginary and perfectly possible — rises out of a new technology, barely in its infancy, that has the potential to explode on society as the new century unfolds. It is called virtual reality, and its proponents say that it could profoundly affect everyday life, as well as business, entertainment and dozens of professions....Said Jaron Lanier, a 32-year-old California computer whiz who coined the term virtual reality: "By the turn of the century, it will no longer be a novelty. It will put movies and television to shame. It will be a tool of the imagination, every child's dream."

Already, simple systems exist that allow a user to enter the world of virtual reality by putting on a headset equipped with small, image-bearing screens. Those systems immerse the user in the sights and sounds of a computer-generated world. By using a specially fitted DataGlove, he or she can even have the experience of touching or moving objects in "virtual space." While American, European, Japanese and Canadian scientists race to develop the technology, architects, psychiatrists, surgeons, pilots and other professionals are finding ways to apply it to their work. Several computer companies already manufacture equipment called image generators that can produce detailed and realistic three-dimensional moving images in full color. Said Henry Fuchs, a computer scientist at the University of North Carolina in Chapel Hill and a leading researcher on virtual reality: "Dozens of people in labs are working on various aspects of the technology."

One early commercial application of virtual reality is in the field of entertainment. Some firms are marketing equipment that lets users play what is, in effect, a glorified video game. In April 1992 Toronto-based Virtuality Canada acquired eight virtual reality systems, at a cost of $60 000 to $85 000 each, from W. Industries Ltd. of Leicester, England. Virtuality introduced the equipment to Canadians at Toronto's annual Canadian National Exhibition in late August, then installed it in two suburban Toronto shopping malls....

To play a Virtuality game, users wear a headset and hold a plastic device called a Spacestick that resembles the handle of a pistol. In one game, called Dactyl Nightmare, the player, immersed in a three-dimensional world, sees a brightly colored platform with staircases leading up to other levels. Outside the platforms and staircases, the background is solid black. At unpredictable intervals, a giant bird resembling a prehistoric pterodactyl swoops towards the player, who can shoot at it by aiming with the Spacestick and firing with a thumb button at the top of the device. As the player moves his arm, a computer-generated image of a hand and a gun makes corresponding movements. Some analysts predict a limitless future for virtual reality as a tool for entertainment....

Cyberspace: Other analysts see a potentially dark side to virtual reality. In his 1984 novel *Neuromancer*, William Gibson, a Vancouver-based science fiction writer, depicts a young man's obsession with a computer-generated universe called cyberspace, a form of virtual reality. Some experts working on the development of Japanese virtual reality systems have predicted that, in a sophisticated form, the new technology could prove addictive, and ultimately dangerous.

Still most proponents contend that the benefits of virtual reality will outweigh any potential risks. Lanier said that by the end of the century virtual reality will be a major form of home entertainment, and that consumer systems will be linked by electronic networks. He predicted that homeowners and their neighbors will enter the same virtual spaces, and interact with each other. Derrick de Kerckhove, director of the McLuhan Program in Culture and Technology at the University of Toronto, added that virtual reality could revolutionize television news programming by allowing viewers the sensation of being immersed in stories such as those about wars and disasters, without suffering the consequences.

But for the most part, scientists and other professionals are devoting themselves to exploring more prosaic applications of virtual reality. Dr. Richard Satava, a surgeon at the Silas B. Hayes Army Hospital in Fort Ord, Calif., said that virtual reality could become a valuable tool to both medical students and practising physicians. Last year, he conducted a gall bladder operation on a computer-generated image of a human torso. Satava said that he and fellow researchers developed a computer program to generate images of a torso and all the organs in a human abdomen. He said that the images were depicted in a simplified form. Satava added that during the simulated operation he wore a headset and DataGlove manufactured by VPL Research Inc., a company founded by Jaron Lanier. As Satava moved the glove, he manipulated a hand within a computer-generated scene, making the necessary incisions to open an abdomen and remove the gall bladder. "I was working with cartoon-level graphics," Satava said. "But our ultimate goal is to produce graphics that are good enough to fool the surgeon."

Visual: American and German military pilots are already immersing themselves in computer-simulated worlds through a helmet-mounted visual display system designed and manufactured by Montreal-based CAE Electronics Ltd., one of the world's leading manufacturers of aviation flight simulators. Charles Gainer, chief of aviation research and development of the U.S. Army Research Institute in Fort Rucker, Ala., said that pilots take training in flight simulators while wearing CAE helmet systems that immerse them in computer-generated airspace. Usually, a pilot sitting in a detailed mockup of an Apache attack helicopter's cockpit wears a helmet that is linked to an image generator. The pilot simulates flying by manipulating two

On Chung and Don Procuniar of CAE Industries Ltd. perform system tests on aircraft simulator

control sticks and he responds to an entirely visual world that he sees through the helmet. A Salt Lake City, Utah, firm, Evans & Sutherland Computer Corp., produces the image generator for the army. Gainer said that with the equipment, a pilot can experience day or night flying in any kind of weather, encounter other traffic in the air or take part in air-to-air or air-to-ground combat. "You can look out the cockpit canopy and see the missile pods and rockets," said Gainer, "but they're not really there."

Virtual reality may play a role in other types of training. Andrea Apara, a vice-president of Fiat Auto SPA in Turin, Italy, said that his company hoped to use virtual reality systems to train workers in the operation and maintenance of sophisticated robotic systems used in car assembly plants. Said Apora: "We can use this technology as a powerful tool." And in Tokyo, Matsushita Electric Works has equipped a Tokyo retail outlet that sells kitchen cabinets, counters and appliances with VPL headsets and gloves. Customers using the virtual reality equipment can immerse themselves in computer-simulated kitchens and even open or close drawers and doors. An inspection through virtual reality can help customers decide whether the components of a kitchen are properly arranged, and whether door handles are the correct height. Company officials said that about 15 customers have bought kitchen units after testing them in virtual reality.

Athletes, too, have turned to virtual reality to enhance their performance. Before the Winter Olympics in Albertville, France, American bobsledder Brian Shimer participated in virtual reality training arranged by Silicon Graphics, Inc. at the company headquarters in Mountain View, Calif., 50 km south of San Francisco. The company programmed a trip down the Albertville bobsled course into its image generator, which is capable of producing three-dimensional color images at a rate of 60 per second. With the image flashing on a six-foot-by-eight-foot screen in front of him and steering a four-man bobsled connected to the image generator, Shimer made the run down the computerized course dozens of times.

Impact: Virtual reality is likely to have a major impact on the entertainment and amusement industries. A Toronto company called The Vivid Group has pioneered what staff members call unencumbered virtual reality. Company co-director Vincent John Vincent, 33, said that the firm's Mandala VR System allows a person to interact with computer-generated images without being immersed in them by wearing a headset. Instead, the user stands in front of a video camera and his image appears on a screen against a background of computer-generated images. By running on the spot, the user appears to be running through a kaleidoscope of changing images. Or he may see images of drums surrounding his image on the screen. He can play the instruments by moving his hands so that his image on the screen strikes the drums, and the Mandala system responds with the sound of a hand striking a drum. The system can be used as an educational tool that allows children to be surrounded by images of letters. They can then practise spelling by picking the letters required to make certain words.

The Vivid Group, which began developing its system 10 years ago, so far has sold 200 units at prices ranging from $7000 to $20 000. One was a

The Vivid Group's Mandala VR System

popular attraction at Canada's pavilion at the Expo '92 world fair in Seville, Spain, said Vincent. The company has also sold a system to one of the Smithsonian Institution museums in Washington, D.C., and installed others for short-term display in about 60 other museums around the world. Said Vincent: "We are creating new universes that people can step into and play with."

Still, while several firms are already making virtual reality available to the public, most proponents of the technology agree that it is so far basically in the development stages. And they say that there are several major technical hurdles to overcome before virtual reality can fulfil its promise. For one thing, the quality of the graphics used in most virtual reality systems is still relatively crude. "Television has raised expectations," said Edward Costello, director of sales and marketing for Vermont-based Polhemus Inc., a high-technology firm. "People expect to see a leaf on every branch instead of figures that look like blocks. Computer graphics have got to catch up with TV." To do that, experts are searching for a way of putting detailed, high-quality images on screens no bigger than a matchbox. "The headsets are too bulky and the screens inside them are the worst possible television screens," said Fuchs. He added that with the technology currently available, it is impossible to display detailed, high-resolution images on small screens. Said Fuchs: "It's like having a million-dollar sound system and playing it through 50-cent speakers."

Disorientation: Most existing virtual reality systems can also cause an unpleasant sensation resembling motion sickness. Costello said that the systems rely on a tracking device that records the movement of a user's head. That mechanism relays the information to the image-generating computer, which in turn produces the corresponding images. The entire process takes just a split second, but even the small time lag can induce disorientation and nausea. Added NASA's Ellis: "I had a headset on for an hour and a half one time. I had the world's greatest splitting headache afterward." But Costello said that last August Polhemus introduced a mechanism to sharply reduce the time needed to track movement and produce new images.

Besides trying to improve the visual side, virtual reality innovators are also searching for more realistic sound. Louis Gehring, a Toronto-based computer graphics expert, says that he has developed a circuit board that puts a feeling of direction and motion into recorded music or sound. Conventional, two-dimensional recorded sound lacks reality, Gehring said, because the listener always knows it is coming out of a speaker. According to Gehring, his device, which he is marketing under the name Focal Point 3D Audio, can make it seem to a listener that an automobile is approaching from a specific direction, and then receding in another.

Despite the amount of development that remains, many scientists working on virtual reality admit to an underlying belief in the potential power of the technology. It is a belief that flows from their dreams of the day when people will routinely switch on a computer and put on a headset to recreate history, examine a microscopic element, experience outer space or go shopping for new dining room furniture. In those dreams, computers are creating worlds that are all but indistinguishable from, and with fewer problems than, the real thing.

New Ideas
That May Change
the Way We Live

◆◆◆

BY

**VALÉRIE ANNE GISCARD D'ESTAING
AND MARK YOUNG**

Ozone Washing Machine

Developed by a team of engineers at Tri-O-Clean Laundry Systems, Inc. of Fort Pierce, Fla., the Tri-O-Clean system is a new washing machine system that cleans clothing without using detergent or hot water, and doesn't drain the water away, but recycles it. Intended for commercial use by large institutions such as hospitals, prisons and hotels, the Tri-O-Clean system uses ozone to clean the wash. An electrical generator pumps ozone into the machine during the wash cycle. The ozone breaks down the organic molecules that comprise stains, dirt and other marks on the laundry, and the force of the water washes the molecules away, leaving the clothes clean. A filter system removes the dirt from the waste water, allowing the water to be recycled. Hot water is not used because the ozone molecules break apart more rapidly at higher temperatures, which would make the system ineffective. A U.S. patent for the system was issued in 1992.

Microwave Clothes Dryer

American Micro-Tech, Inc. is developing a microwave clothes dryer. In June 1992 Southern California Edison announced that it had tested a prototype that met U.S. Department of Energy standards. The device, covered by patents in Canada, Japan and the United States, uses 10 percent less energy than conventional electric dryers, operating at lower temperatures with shorter running cycles. Commercial development is some years away.

Antipollution Artificial Lake

In 1992 David P. Murray received a U.S. patent for an artificial lake designed to erase the problems of pollutants caused by water runoff from residential development. Chemicals used to fertilize lawns or protect building materials often show up in water supplies as a result of runoff following heavy rainfalls. Murray, an aquatic biologist, devised an artificial lake that uses plants, such as pondweeds, to absorb these chemicals. Murray's lake features a flat plateau in the center, where the plants can be cultivated and also cropped if they begin to choke the water system. A trench forms a boundary around the lake, which contains plants, such as coontail, that fight algae.

Odor Genes

A team of researchers at Johns Hopkins University, led by Solomon H. Snyder, received a U.S. patent in 1992 for the gene of a protein they had identified that may be able to help in restoring or enhancing an individual's sense of smell. Experiments have shown that the protein attaches itself to various odor-causing molecules, and transports them to receptors at the back of the nose. It may have applications for people who have lost their sense of smell, such as the elderly and patients undergoing chemotherapy.

Memory Plastics

The Japanese group Nippon Zeon is developing a plastic with a memory. It has the same properties as the metal alloys, but thanks to a greater molecular mass and to its particular chemical links, it is as elastic as rubber. So, for example, in the future dented car fenders will reshape themselves when heated to the temperature of manufacture. It may be the super-material of the future.

X-ray Camera

Using technology developed since the 1960s, engineers from Philips N.V. and a team of biologists from the French National Center for Scientific Research, in association with the French National Museum of

Natural History, developed a high-speed 16 mm camera using X-rays. X-ray photography makes it possible to analyze the movements of athletes and small animals. The camera can take up to 500 pictures per second.

Imax Solido
First demonstrated at EXPO '90 in Osaka, Japan, IMAX Solido is the first motion picture system to present full-color 3-D images on a wide-field dome screen. The 3-D images extend in front, above and to the side of the viewer, who observes the screen through cordless electronic liquid crystal glasses. The glasses work as electronic shutters and are synchronized with the projector, decoding the left and right eye images projected onto the screen, giving the effect of stereoscopic viewing. At EXPO '92 in Seville, Spain, the film *Echoes of the Sun,* a 20-minute film telling the story of photosynthesis, was used to demonstrate IMAX Solido.

The Prometheus System
The Prometheus system was launched in 1986 and is the most ambitious of all the in-car computer-guided driving systems currently being developed. A joint European effort, the goal of Prometheus is to reduce the problems of traffic congestion, pollution and safety. Three prototypes have been unveiled, including one system that could see through fog using an infrared camera and project onto the windshield road conditions ahead. A computer would assess whether the car was proceeding safely and would automatically slow it down if it believed the situation to be dangerous. Another function uses an on-board computer that logs into a city's system. This system would tell the driver which roads were congested, where parking is available and even which hotels had vacancies. Some of these devices could be ready by 1995, but it is expected that Prometheus will not be fully operational until the next century.

Hypersonics
Several European countries and the United States are finding projects to develop a hypersonic aircraft. In the United States, President Ronald Reagan drew national attention to the Orient Express, otherwise known as the X-30, which would make it possible to fly from Washington, D.C., to Tokyo, Japan, in 2 1/2 hours. These space aircraft projects raise numerous technical problems, notably the

speed/overheating ratio, as the sound barrier is also the heat barrier. Another problem is propulsion. Engineers are currently studying the use of the ramjet engine as the best means to power a hypersonic craft. It is unlikely we will see such craft in operation before 2015.

The Molecular Computer

A team of Japanese engineers is developing a computer based on the stereochemical characteristics of certain molecules. It is estimated that if successful, the computer would have unlimited possibilities in terms of storage capacity and speed. Their research is already well advanced. The team has created a derivative of benzene, Ocah, whose optical properties change according to the angle formed by the eye and the two "poles" of the molecule, which means it can be either straight or bent, and its reaction to light is different in either case. Engineers then compared the two states, trans and cis, by binary means using a computer. The main problem with this was that the cis state is unstable and, consequently, memory was uncertain. This problem was solved by "balancing" the molecule by passing an electric current through it.

The implications of this technology are too broad to imagine them all. At an earlier stage, molecular electronics allowed calculations 10 000 times faster than the fastest computers. As for storage capacity, it will be hundreds of millions of bits per square inch in laser print, limited only to the size of the latter. Using procedures such as the tunnel effect, it may be possible to reach one billion bits on the same surface.

More Future Stuff

◆ ◆ ◆

BY

MALCOLM ABRAMS
AND HARRIET BERNSTEIN

<table>
<tr><td colspan="2">TV THAT PUTS YOU IN
THE PICTURE</td></tr>
<tr><td>ODDS</td><td>100%</td></tr>
<tr><td>ETA</td><td>1992</td></tr>
<tr><td>PRICE</td><td>$11 500</td></tr>
</table>

Vivid Effects TV puts you on the screen to interact in video worlds.

- The next time you watch "Cheers," pull up a bar stool next to Norm and Cliffy.
- Care for a game of tennis…with your friend who lives in Los Angeles, 2000 miles [3220 km] away? Call him or her up. "Tennis, anyone…" You'll both be there on your TV screens, on an animated tennis court, rackets in hand, whacking the ball back and forth.
- Buy the new hockey, basketball, or baseball video game. See all those little players moving around on the video. "Hey, wait a minute…one of them is me!"
- Step up to the bandstand. Take your place behind the drums. Pick up the sticks and hit those skins. Play any song you like. Yet the instrument exists only in videoland.

- Making an important business presentation? Lots of graphs and pie charts on video. Now add you...walking up to those graphs, pulling pieces out of those pie charts. Knock their corporate black socks off!

Back in 1983, two college students at the University of Waterloo in Ontario, Canada, started kicking around some concepts with a video camera, a computer, a TV, and some other stuff. Today they are the Vivid Effects Company of Toronto, creator of the Mandala System of animated video worlds and right up there on the cutting edge of virtual-reality technology.

Vincent John Vincent, a thirty-one-year-old psychologist, is president of Vivid Effects. Frank MacDougall, twenty-eight, is "the computer genius behind it all." Together, what they've created has been hailed as sensational from Washington to Tokyo.

And starting in 1992, for about the price of an inexpensive family sedan, you'll be able to buy the system for your living room. What you'll get, Vincent explains, "is a full system wired together that includes five different screens, a camera, TV, computer, and synthesizers." And, of course, the patented video digitizing processing equipment and software called the Mandala System.

When you get all this stuff home, you might want to start with something easy, like the hockey goalie game (on display at the National Hockey League Hall of Fame in Toronto, by the way). On the TV screen, you see the posts and hockey net. Now step in front of the video camera set up in your living room. Suddenly, there you are, digitized, looking every inch the hockey goaltender, standing in front of the goal mouth. Move your right arm in the living room, the little man on the screen moves his right arm. Now what?

Suddenly, swooping into the picture is a fierce-looking animated player. He brings his stick back and fires the puck 90 miles [145 km] an hour. Oh no! Aw, but the fearless goaltender (you!) kicks out his right leg and miraculously stops the puck just before it enters the net. The crowd cheers. But wait, here comes another puck, and it's aimed right at your head...

Get the picture?

"What's really unique," says Vincent, "is the combination of everything — a standard video camera that's brought into a computer system, that has a graphical base to it so we can digitize people's images in live, real-time video so they can see themselves on a television screen and they're a part of the television world.

"It's sort of like being with a live Roger Rabbit," Vincent chuckles.

◆ ◆ ◆

THE HANDYMAN ROBOT

ODDS	70%
ETA	1997
PRICE	$15 000

Now here's the robot we've all been waiting for ever since robotics and artificial intelligence became modern-day buzz words. This cute little R2D2 lookalike will prepare meals, mow the lawn, vacuum floors, fetch the newspaper, and pour drinks — all without pay, complaint, or commitment.

It's voice activated (and you only have to ask once), knows dozens of tasks, and can be "taught" to learn more, like making your favorite pasta sauce. And while you sleep, this robot will roam your abode, serving as an all-night sentry.

Droid Genesis I is the name, and for $15 000, he/she/it is a bargain. "Simplifying people's lives," is what it's all about, according to Robert Danial, president of Droid Systems, the New York City company that is developing this household robot. And while there may be a few robots already on the market, they're mere "toys," says Danial. "They can carry a drink around on a tray — but they have no intelligence and no strength."

What constitutes intelligence in a machine is still open to debate, but Danial feels Droid Genesis I will come closer to replicating human behavior than any robot so far. "We really take for granted complex and numerous steps that happen, for example, between feeling a hot stove and removing our hand. In that action a lot of information is transmitted from the hand to the brain.

"With artificial intelligence, we model, simplify and replicate how the human mind goes about performing tasks — from vision to speech to hearing to sensing, even to smelling. Then we process that information and obtain 'intelligent' results."

The present state of Droid Genesis I is partly in the workshop and partly on the drawing board. Danial admits that while the body is set to go, the brain (i.e., the software) is still being developed.

The body is 4 feet, 6 inches tall [137 cm], weighs 180 pounds [81 kg], and can lift up to 15 pounds [6 kg].

By the turn of the century, Droids could be as much at home in our homes as we are. "A robot will start out as a novelty," says Danial, "then it will become something we can't live without."

◆ ◆ ◆

BLUE ROSES	
ODDS	90%
ETA	1995
PRICE	$100 Per Stem

The gift of a dozen red roses is a statement of passionate love. What a bouquet of blue roses will represent is up for grabs, because they're still on the genetic drawing board.

Perhaps blue roses will signify sadness. When you have the "blues," send them to the man or woman who broke your heart. More likely, blue roses will stand for "broke," as in $100 a piece or $1200 a dozen.

That's the anticipated selling price in today's dollars when blue roses turn up for sale at your neighborhood florist shop. "In flowers, novelty has value," explained Michael Dalling, president of Calgene Pacific, the Melbourne, Australia, company that's developing the new roses in a joint venture with a Japanese firm, Suntory.

Nationalism is another reason Calgene Pacific expects to get top dollar for blue roses. The American flag, the Australian flag, the British flag — they're all red, white, and blue. Just imagine the rose decorations on the fourth of July or the twenty-fourth of May (Queen Victoria's Birthday).

Ahhh, but the roses aren't here yet. In Melbourne, genetic engineers are working to purify an enzyme that is missing in roses but accounts for blue color in other flowers, such as petunias. Once the enzyme is purified, the gene to produce it will be cloned and inserted into rose plants. The altered plant will pass on its blue color to its progeny, ensuring future blue generations.

The roses will not only be beautiful, we're assured they will last longer. Calgene Pacific is developing a technique to block the production of ethylene, a substance naturally produced by flowers that leads to wilting after they're cut.

◆ ◆ ◆

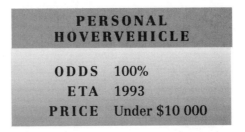

PERSONAL HOVERVEHICLE

ODDS	100%
ETA	1993
PRICE	Under $10 000

I'm flying. I'm flyyyyinnngggg...even if I'm only 8 inches off the ground.

And so what if it is a Hovervehicle. Don't knock it. You don't need a pilot's license, you can store it in your backyard, and it costs less than most cars. Try finding an airplane to fit that bill.

Hovercraft™ are not new. In fact, the idea has been around for more than a century. And huge Hovercraft have been carrying people across the English Channel for years.

But we're talking about a snappy little personal Hovervehicle built for two. It's called the RX2000 and comes in colors like Ferrari Red and Sunshine Yellow.

The RX2000's manufacturer, HoverDynamics of Cumming, Georgia, wants you to think in terms of recreational vehicles, not ferryboats. New materials and engine technology have made the personal Hovervehicle — small, low cost, stylish, and reliable — a reality.

The RX2000 has an impressive range of capabilities. It can zoom over land, water, ice, or snow with equanimity because it's supported on a cushion of air while moving, never touching a surface. However, if you land on water, it floats. Great for fishing!

Actually a small Hovervehicle is good for a lot of things, from wave jumping to search-and-rescue missions. In this latter capacity, nothing can navigate marshy wetlands, broken ice, and deep snow like a Hovervehicle.

The RX2000 is easy to drive, flies for three hours on six gallons [27 L] of gas, does up to 48 miles [77 km] per hour, and can climb a 35-degree incline. It's 13 feet [3.9 m] long, 7.25 feet [2.1 m] wide, and weighs 520 pounds [234 kg]. It carries two adults or a payload of 450 pounds [202 kg].

In a few years, personal Hovervehicles should be as common as speedboats. HoverDynamics is already working on a five-passenger model so you can take the kids.

Elephants

♦♦♦

BY

PATRICK

LANE

The cracked cedar bunkhouse
hangs behind me like a grey pueblo
in the sundown where I sit
to carve an elephant
from a hunk of brown soap
for the Indian boy who lives
in the village a mile back
in the bush.

The alcoholic truck-driver
and the cat-skinner sit beside me
with their eyes closed
all of us waiting out the last hour
until we go back on the grade

and I try to forget the forever
clank clank clank
across the grade
pounding stones and earth to powder
for hours in mosquito darkness
of the endless cold mountain night.

The elephant takes form —
my knife caresses smooth soap
scaling off curls of brown
which the boy saves to take home
to his mother in the village

Finished, I hand the carving to him
and he looks at the image of the great
beast for a long time
then sets it on dry cedar
and looks up at me:
            What's an elephant?

he asks
so I tell him of the elephants
and their jungles. The story
of the elephant graveyard
which no one has ever found
and how the silent
animals of the rain forest
go away to die somewhere
in the limberlost of distances
and he smiles

tells me of his father's
graveyard where his people have been
buried for years. So far back
no one remembers when it started
and I ask him where the graveyard is
and he tells me it is gone
now where no one will ever find it
buried under the grade of the new
highway.

Our Mother
the Earth
Is Growing
Old Now

♦♦♦

FROM THE

IROQUOIS CONFEDERACY

The Haudenosaunee, or Six Nations Iroquois Confederacy, is among the most ancient continuously operating governments in the world. Long before the arrival of the European peoples in North America, our people met in council to enact the principles of peaceful coexistence among nations and the recognition of the right of peoples to a continued and uninterrupted existence. European people left our council fires and journeyed forth into the world to spread principles of justice and democracy which they learned from us and which have had profound effects upon the evolution of the Modern World....

Brothers and Sisters: When the Europeans first invaded our lands, they found a world filled with the bountiful gifts of creation....Everywhere the game was plentiful, and sometimes the birds darkened the sky like great clouds, so great were their numbers. Our country teemed with elk and deer, bear and moose, and we were a happy and prosperous people in those times.

Brothers and Sisters: Our Mother the Earth is growing old now. No longer does she support upon her breast the teeming herds of wildlife who once shared this place with us, and most of the great forest which is our home is gone today. The forest was butchered a century ago to make charcoal for the forges of the Industrial Revolution, most of the game was destroyed by sport hunters and farmers, most of the bird life has been destroyed by hunters and pesticides which are common this century. Many of the rivers flow thick with the effluence of great population centers throughout the country. We see the "scorched earth" policy has not ended.

Brothers and Sisters: We are alarmed at the evidence that is before us. The smoke from industrial centers in the Midwest around the Great Lakes rises in a deadly cloud and returns to earth in the form of acid rains over the Adirondack Mountains, and the fish life cannot reproduce in the acid waters. In the high country of the Adirondack Mountains, the lakes are still, the fish are no more.

The people who plant the lands that we have occupied for thousands of years display no love for the life of this place. Each year they plant the same crops on the same lands and they must then spray those crops with poisons to kill the insects which naturally infest their fields because they do not rotate crops or allow the land to rest. Their pesticides kill the bird life, and the runoff poisons the surface waters.

They must spray also the other plant life with herbicides, and each year the runoff from the fields carries these poisons into the watersheds of our country and into the waters of the world.

Brothers and Sisters: Our ancient homeland is spotted today with an array of chemical dumps. Along the Niagara River, dioxin, a particularly deadly substance, threatens the remaining life there and in the waters which flow from there. Forestry departments spray the surviving forests with powerful insecticides to encourage tourism by people seeking a few days or weeks away from the cities where the air hangs heavy with sulphur and carbon oxides. The insecticides kill the black flies, but also destroy much of the food chain for the bird, fish and animal life which also inhabit those regions.

The fish of the Great Lakes are laced with mercury from industrial plants, and fluoride from aluminum plants poisons the land and the people. Sewage from the population centers is mixed with PCBs and PBS in the watershed of the Great Lakes and the Finger Lakes, and the waters are virtually nowhere safe for any living creature.

Brothers and Sisters: We are alarmed that a string of nuclear power plants is being built around our country and that at Three Mile Island in the southern portion of our ancient territories an "accident" has occurred which is of a type of accident which could hasten the end of life in this place. We are dismayed that a nuclear waste dump at West Valley (N.Y.) upstream from one of our communities is releasing radioactive substances through our lands and into the watershed of Lake Erie. We are offended that the information about the nature of these plants is known only to the highest officials of the United States, leaving the people unarmed to defend themselves from such development and the development of nuclear power is encouraged to continue.

We are concerned for the well-being and continued survival of our brothers and sisters in the Southwest and Northwest who are exposed to uranium mining and its inherent dangers. The mining end is the dirtiest portion of the nuclear fuel cycle and has progressed beyond questions of whether or not the machinery is dependable. Already vast amounts of low-level radioactive uranium tailings have been dumped in cities and used in building materials of dwellings and public buildings over a wide area of the Southwest. People have died, and many more can be expected to die.

Proponents of the Nuclear Fuel Cycle issue statement after statement to the people, urging that the nuclear reactors are fitted with safety devices so sophisticated that a meltdown is only the most remote of possibilities. Yet we observe that no machinery or other invention made by human hands was a permanent thing. Nothing humans ever built, not even the pyramids of Egypt, maintained their purpose indefinitely. The only universal truth applicable to human-made devices is that all of them fail in their turn. Nuclear reactors must also fall victim to that truth.

Brothers and Sisters: We cannot adequately express our feelings of horror and repulsion as we view the policies of industry and government in North America which threaten to destroy all life. Our forefathers predicted that the European Way of Life would bring a Spiritual imbalance to the world, that the Earth would grow old as a result of that imbalance. Now it is before all the world to see — that the life-producing forces are being reversed, and that the life-potential is leaving this land. Only a people whose minds are twisted beyond an ability to perceive truth could act in ways which will threaten the future generations of humanity.

Brothers and Sisters: We point out to you the Spiritual Path of Righteousness and Reason. We bring to your thought and minds that right-minded human beings seek to promote above all else the life of all things. We direct to your minds that peace is not merely the absence of war, but the constant effort to maintain harmonious existence between all peoples, from individual to individual and between humans and the other beings of this planet. We point out to you that a Spiritual Consciousness is the Path to Survival of Humankind. We who walk about on Mother Earth occupy this place for only a short time. It is our duty as human beings to preserve the life that is here for the benefit of the generations yet unborn.

Brothers and Sisters: The Haudenosaunee are determined to take whatever actions we can to halt the destruction of Mother Earth. In our territories, we continue to carry out our function as spiritual caretakers of the land. In this role as caretakers we cannot, and will not, stand idly by while the future of the coming generations is being systematically destroyed. We recognize that the fight is a long one and that we cannot hope to win it alone. To win, to secure the future, we must join hands with like-minded people and create a strength through unity. We commemorate two hundred years of injustice and the destruction of the world with these words.

The
Earth
Charter

♦ ♦ ♦

This Charter was prepared by the non-governmental organizations (NGOs) gathered in Rio de Janeiro during the Earth Summit, 1992.

PREAMBLE

. . . .

We are Earth, the people, plants and animals, rains and oceans, breath of the forest and flow of the sea. We honour Earth as the home of all living things. We cherish Earth's beauty and diversity of life. We welcome Earth's ability to renew as being the basis of all life. We recognize the special place of Earth's Indigenous Peoples, their territories, their customs and their unique relationship to Earth. We are appalled at the human suffering, poverty and damage to Earth caused by inequality of power.

We accept a shared responsibility to protect and restore Earth and to allow wise and equitable use of resources so as to achieve an ecological balance and new social, economic and spiritual values.

In all our diversity we are one. Our common home is increasingly threatened.

We thus commit ourselves to the following principles, noting at all times the particular needs of women, indigenous peoples, the South, the disabled and all those who are disadvantaged:

PRINCIPLES

1. We agree to respect, encourage, protect and restore Earth's ecosystems to ensure biological and cultural diversity.

2. We recognize our diversity and our common partnership. We respect all cultures and affirm the rights of all people to basic environmental needs.

3. Poverty affects us all. We agree to alter unsustainable patterns of production and consumption to ensure the eradication of poverty and to end the abuse of Earth. This must include a recognition of the role of debt and financial flows from the South to the North and opulence and corruption as primary causes. We shall emphasize and improve the endogenous capacity for technology creation and development. Attempts to eradicate poverty should not be a mandate to abuse the environment and attempts to protect or restore the environment should not ignore basic human needs.

4. We recognize that national barriers do not generally conform to Earth's ecological realities. National sovereignty does not mean sanctuary from our collective responsibility to protect and restore Earth's ecosystems. Trade practices and transnational corporations must not cause environmental degradation and should be controlled in order to achieve social justice, equitable trade and solidarity with ecological principles.

5. We reject the build-up and use of military force and the use of economic pressure as means of resolving conflict. We commit ourselves to pursue genuine peace, which is not merely the absence of war but includes the eradication of poverty, the promotion of social justice and economic, spiritual, cultural and ecological well-being.

6. We agree to ensure that decision-making processes and their criteria are clearly defined, transparent, explicit, accessible and equitable. Those whose decisions or activities may affect the environment must first prove the absence of harm. Those likely to be affected, particularly populations in the South and those in subjugation within existing States, should have free access to information and effectively participate in the decision-making processes.

7. States, institutions, corporations and peoples are unequal in their contribution to environmental harm, experience of ecological degradation and ability to respond to environmental destruction. While all are responsible for improving environmental quality, those who have expropriated or consumed the majority of Earth's resources or who continue to do so must cease such expropriation or reduce such consumption and must bear the costs of ecological restoration and protection by providing the majority of financial and technological resources.

8. Women constitute over half of Earth's human population. They are a powerful source for change. They contribute more than half the effort to human welfare. Men and women agree that women's status in decision-making and social processes must equitably reflect their contribution. We must shift from a society dominated by men to one which more accurately reflects the valued contributions of men and women to human ecological welfare. We have come to realise that the threats to the biosphere which sustains all life on Earth have increased in rate, magnitude and scale to such extent that inaction would be negligent.

EARTH CHARTER ACTION PLAN

1. We shall adopt the spirit and principles of the Earth Charter at the individual level and through concrete actions within our non-governmental organizations.

2. We will use existing mechanisms and/or create an international network of the signatories hereto to disseminate the Earth Charter as principles for action at the local, national and global level.

3. The Earth Charter shall be translated into all the languages of Earth.

4. We shall commit ourselves to the preparation of "Objective 1995" by which the United Nations will celebrate its 50th anniversary, at which time we want them to adopt this Earth Charter.

5. Non-governmental organizations worldwide shall initiate a combined campaign "We Are Earth" through to 1995 and the adoption of this Earth Charter by the United Nations.

6. Every individual, organization, corporation and state shall dedicate a percentage of their operating budget and their profit as an "Earth Percentage" dedicated to the restoration, protection and management of Earth's ecosystems and the promotion of equitable development.

7. We call for a second Global Forum to be held in 1999 to evaluate and reaffirm our commitment to the relationships made, the accomplishments achieved and the goals sought at this 1992 Global Forum.

Betting On Planet Earth

◆◆◆

BY

JOHN

TIERNEY

In 1980 an ecologist and an economist bet $1000 over the future price of five metals. At stake was much more — a view of the planet's ultimate limits, a vision of humanity's destiny. One saw farm silos brimming with record harvests; the other saw topsoil eroding and pesticide seeping into groundwater. One saw people living longer; the other saw rain forests being decimated.

Today these two men lead two intellectual schools — sometimes called the doomsters and the boomsters — that debate whether the world is getting better or going to the dogs.

The ecologist, Paul R. Ehrlich, 59, has been one of the world's better-known scientists since publishing *The Population Bomb* in 1968. More than two million copies were sold. When he is not teaching at Stanford University in California or studying butterflies, Ehrlich can be found lecturing, collecting an award or appearing on the "Today" show. He is the pessimist.

The Population Bomb began: "The battle to feed all of humanity is over. In the 1970s hundreds of millions of people are going to starve to death." Ehrlich wrote that "nothing can prevent a substantial increase in the world death rate." In 1974 he predicted that "before 1985 mankind will enter an age of scarcity" in which "the accessible supplies of many key minerals will be nearing depletion."

The economist, Julian L. Simon, also 59, is a professor at the University of Maryland, whose views have helped shape policy in Washington for the past decade. But he has never enjoyed Ehrlich's academic success or popular appeal. He is the optimist.

Simon believes that population growth constitutes not a crisis, but a boon that will ultimately mean a cleaner environment, a healthier humanity and more abundant supplies of food and raw materials. Tomorrow's world will be better because it will have more people producing more bright ideas. Progress can go on indefinitely because the planet's resources are actually not finite.

When Simon wrote about his vision of the future in *Science* magazine in 1980, his article drew a spate of angry letters. An irate Ehrlich provided the simple arithmetic: The planet's resources had to be divided among a population then growing at the rate of 75 million people a year, outstripping the earth's supplies of food, fresh water and minerals. As resources became scarcer, it was inevitable "that commodities must become expensive."

Simon responded with a challenge. Let anyone pick any natural resource — grain, oil, coal, timber, metals — and any future date. If the resource really were to become scarcer as the world's population grew, then its price should rise. Simon wanted to bet that the price would instead decline.

Ehrlich accepted Simon's offer. In October 1980 he bet $1000 on five metals: chrome, copper, nickel, tin and tungsten. If the 1990 combined prices, corrected for inflation, turned out to be higher than $1000, Simon would pay him the difference. If

prices fell, then Ehrlich would pay Simon.

Ehrlich was right about world population. It is now 5.3 billion, 1.8 billion more than it was when he published *The Population Bomb*. Yet somehow the average person is healthier and wealthier. Infant mortality has declined, and life expectancy has increased, most dramatically in the Third World. There have been famines in countries afflicted by war, drought and disastrous agricultural policies, but overall food production has outpaced population. The day of reckoning will have to be rescheduled.

Ehrlich's is such an obvious proposition in a finite world; things run out. The counterargument is not as intuitively convincing. It has generally consisted of a simple question: Why haven't things run out yet?

When Julian Simon heard the grim predictions about overpopulation in the late 1960s, he began writing on the need to persuade women to have fewer babies. But then he read studies showing that, overall, the countries with rapid population growth were not suffering more than other countries. In fact, many were doing better.

He also came across evidence that the price of natural resources since 1870 had fallen in real terms. The average worker today could buy more coal with an hour's pay than he could in the last century, just as he could buy more food. Things were actually getting *less* scarce as population grew.

Simon and some other economists looked back at 10 000 years of resource crises and saw a pattern: As things became more scarce people responded with innovations. They found new supplies or practised conservation.

Often the scarcity led to a much better substitute. The Greeks' transition from the Bronze Age to the Iron Age 3000 years ago was inspired by a disruption of trade. A shortage of the tin needed to make bronze led the Greeks to try iron. Similarly, timber shortages in 16th-century Britain ushered in the age of coal.

Temporary shortages do occur, but Simon and other boomsters argue that as long as government doesn't interfere — by mandating conservation or setting price controls — people will find alternatives.

In his 1981 book, *The Ultimate Resource,* Simon wrote that human ingenuity could indefinitely expand the planet's carrying capacity. This idea marked a crucial difference between Simon and Ehrlich: the view of the world not as a closed ecosystem, but as a flexible marketplace.

Simon conceded that the marketplace did need some regulation. But North America's air and water have been getting cleaner for decades, partly because richer societies can afford to pay for pollution controls, and partly because of technology — the pollution in our cities from cars is minimal compared to the soot from coal-burning furnaces and the solid waste from horses at the turn of the century.

Simon insists that environmental crises are exaggerated. "As soon as one predicted disaster doesn't occur, the doomsters skip to another," he complains. "There's nothing wrong with them worrying about new problems — but why don't they see that, in the aggregate, things are getting better? They deny our creative powers for solutions."

Simon's fiercest battle has been against Ehrlich's idea that the world has too many people. Simon acknowledges that rising population causes short-term problems, but he maintains that there are long-term benefits when those children become productive, resourceful adults. He attacked Ehrlich for suggesting that government use coercion to limit family size and to cut off food aid to countries that refuse to control population growth.

Among academics, Simon seems to be gaining in the debate. Many scientists are uncomfortable with his sweeping optimism, but the consensus has been shifting against Ehrlich's idea of population growth as the great evil.

Simon is still far behind, however, when it comes to winning over the general public. Prior to Earth Day in 1990, Ehrlich was on television promoting his new book, *The Population Explosion,* which declares that "the population bomb has detonated." At an Earth Day rally in Washington a crowd of more than 100 000 applauded when Ehrlich said that population growth could produce a world in which their grandchildren would endure food riots in the streets of America.

That same day, a block away in a small conference room, Simon called population growth "a victory over death" because of the doubling of life expectancy since the Industrial Revolution. "This is an incredible gain. You'd expect lovers of human life to be jumping with joy," he said. "Instead, they're lamenting that so many people are alive." Only 16 people were in the audience to celebrate Simon's message.

The bet was settled last fall without ceremony. Ehrlich simply mailed Simon a sheet of calculations about metal prices — along with a cheque for $576.07. Each of the five metals chosen by Ehrlich's group, when adjusted for inflation since 1980, had declined in price.

Prices fell, in part, for the same reasons they had fallen in previous decades — entrepreneurship and continuing technological improvements. Prospectors discovered new lodes. Thanks to computers, new machines and new chemical processes, there were more efficient ways to extract and refine the ores.

For many uses, metals were replaced by cheaper materials, notably plastics. Phone calls went through satellites and fibre-optic lines instead of copper wires. Ceramics replaced tungsten in cutting tools.

Is there a lesson here for the future? "Absolutely not," said Ehrlich. "I have no doubt that in the next century, if we let the ecological systems keep running downhill, we could have a gigantic population crash."

Simon was not surprised to hear about his opponent's reaction. "So Ehrlich is talking about a population crash," he said. "That sounds like an even better way to make money. I'll give him heavy odds on that one."

A 3-frame sequence of the Earth rise over the Moon's horizon, taken from the Apollo 10 Lunar Module

We Have Forgotten Who We Are

♦♦♦

FROM THE
U.N. ENVIRONMENTAL
SABBATH PROGRAM

We have forgotten who we are.

We have forgotten who we are
We have alienated ourselves from the unfolding of the cosmos
We have become estranged from the movements of the earth
We have turned our backs on the cycles of life.

We have forgotten who we are.

We have sought only our own security
We have exploited simply for our own ends
We have distorted our knowledge
We have abused our power.

We have forgotten who we are.

Now the land is barren
And the waters are poisoned
And the air is polluted.

We have forgotten who we are.

Now the forests are dying
And the creatures are disappearing
And humans are despairing.

We have forgotten who we are.

We ask forgiveness
We ask for the gift of remembering
We ask for the strength to change.

We have forgotten who we are.

What I Did
During My
Park Vacation

◆◆◆

BY

RUTH

BERMAN

When the park comes to the neighborhood all the floors drop down a couple centimeters, and all the elevators are out of joint. Everyone trips getting out.

If you are carrying your tea ration, this can be serious.

But no one minds, because the park is on the roof, and lying snug against the flat lines of roof-tiling and conveyor-belts.

Usually, no one goes up to the top of the shaft, except the top-floorers, and from there no one crosses into the surface-hydraul to get shoved up to the very roof except the janitors who have to clear filters, or adjust solars, or take in deliveries from the belts. But when the park is there, everyone goes up by turns, higher even than the roof, onto the green.

And it's green forever, green, and flowers, and trees as tall as grownups.

They don't let you climb them, though. They say they aren't big enough. Which is pretty weird, actually, because when you ask when they'll be big enough, they say that's as big as they go, on account of the roots are so far down as they can go, down to the rooftops. But kids in old stories are always climbing trees.

I mean, not always, but lots.

When the park comes to the neighborhood, the air at home gets stuffy, because your power gets piped in from other people's solars. But it's all right, because you can go play in the park, where there's lots of fresh air, which is what air is when it smells open and it keeps changing direction instead of circulating properly.

Deliveries get kind of uncertain, too, and have to be detoured in from groundlevel.

But up in the park flowers grow right out in the open, without pots, or tanks, or anything. Roses and peonies, and narcissus, and all kinds. They look nice. You can pick them, if there are enough and they're giving out permits.

Then they die. The flowers. That is nature.

Nature is very good for you, and I like it very much. During my park vacation I saw lots of nature. Then they rolled the park over onto the tops of the next buildings. The park circulates, just like real air. It is nice to have it visit. I like to take my tea ration up on the park, but I didn't this time, because I'd spilled it. The green wasn't as green, and it bothered me more about the Keep Off the Trees signs, but it was still nice.

Someday the trees will get bigger, I bet, and I will hide in one and go with the park all over the district, maybe all over the region, and never come down again.

Unless I grow up first. I bet even if a tree got twice as tall as a grownup, a grownup wouldn't fit in it. Not for hiding. And it would be bad for the tree, maybe.

But I could do it okay, if the trees would get a little bigger.

Trees have leaves, except when they have needles. Some trees have nuts. Some have fruit. You can eat them, if you get a permit. When I go with the park I'll live in a jonathan apple tree.

You'll see.

The Boy with Five Fingers

◆◆◆

BY

JAMES GUNN

I love Miss Harrison. The other boys laugh at me and say that Miss Davis is prettier or Miss Spencer is nicer. But I don't care. I love Miss Harrison.

Miss Harrison's my teacher. When I grow up we're going to get married. When I tell her that she gets that kind of crinkling around her eye like she does when she's pleased about something, and she says that's fine like she meant it, and I guess she does.

The first time I thought about it was the day Miss Harrison told us about the scientists and the Old Race and the Basic Right. Miss Harrison said we should try to keep track of what the scientists are doing because they are the wisest and maybe if we know more about them we will be wiser, too, and might even be scientists ourselves some day. But I think what she really wanted to talk about was the Basic Right. Somehow, everyday, she talks about the Basic Right and it must be important because she talks about it so much.

So Miss Harrison said that many, many years ago, before any of us were born, the scientists had uncovered ruins and nobody knew what they were and everybody wondered and thought about them because they were really big.

Somebody said that we had built them long ago and left them and forgotten about them but nobody believed that because we live in little houses far apart and we never had built anything as big as the ruins and never had wanted to build anything like that.

Then somebody else said that the ruins had been built by a race that lived on Earth before we did and had died or something because maybe conditions got different or maybe they went to live on another planet. And everybody said that must be right, so they started calling them the Old Race but nobody knew what they looked like or did, or anything except that they built these huge places and then went away.

Nobody knew any more than that for years and years, Miss Harrison said, until just a year or so ago when the scientists dug up a place that wasn't all in ruins and found statues and pictures and books and everything. So everybody was all excited and worked on them awfully hard until they could tell what the Old Race was like and just about what was in the books.

Miss Harrison kind of stopped here and looked at us like she does when she's going to tell us something important and we should all get real quiet and listen carefully so we wouldn't miss anything.

Then she said that they had just released the news and the Old Race wasn't really different after all but sort of like ancestors of ours only far away. She said that in lots of ways they were like us only strange and did strange things, and she said we should be sorry for them and glad, too, because maybe if they hadn't been strange we wouldn't be here. Then she told us how strange they were, and I was glad I didn't live then and that I was living now and I was in Miss Harrison's class and listening to her tell us about the Old Race.

Most all of them lived together in these big places, she said, like ants in an ant heap. Everybody gasped at that because we all liked lots of room. But the strangest thing of all, Miss Harrison said, was something else. She stopped again and we all got real quiet. They were all, she said slowly, exactly alike.

Nobody said anything for a moment and then Willie began to laugh the way he does, sort of half-hissing, and pretty soon we were all laughing and Miss Harrison, too. They all had two eyes, she said, and one nose, and one mouth, and two ears, and two arms and two legs. After every one of those things Willie began hissing again and we all had to laugh. And, Miss Harrison said, they were all stuck in exactly the same place. Their arms and legs all had bones in them that had joints in the middle and at each end.

Though they were all exactly alike, Miss Harrison said, they thought they could see differences and because of this they did all sorts of strange things until they did the strangest thing of all and ruined all their big places and their children weren't all alike any more. So it went on like that until nobody was alike and here we are. So they were kind of ancestors, like Miss Harrison said.

Then Miss Harrison stopped again and got up slow, the way she does when she wants to make sure everybody will pay attention. We all held our breath. In this room, she said, right now, we have a member of the Old Race.

Everybody let out his breath all at once. We all looked at her but she laughed and said no, she wasn't it. Johnny, she said, stand up, and I stood up. There, said Miss Harrison, is what the Old Race looked like. Everybody stared at me and I felt kind of cold and lonely all at once. Of course, she said, I don't mean Johnny is really one of the Old Race but he looks just like they used to and he even has five fingers on each hand.

All at once I felt ashamed. I put my hands behind me where nobody could see.

Willie started hissing again, but he wasn't laughing now and his thin forked tongue was flickering at me. Everybody moved as far away from me as they could get and started making nasty sounds. If I had been a little younger I might have started to cry, but I just stood there and wished I had a mouth and tongue like Willie's, or a cart like Louise's instead of legs, or arms like Joan's or fingers like Mike's.

But Miss Harrison stood up straight and frowned, like she does when she's real mad about something and she said she was very surprised and it would seem like everything she'd said had been wasted. Pretty soon everybody quieted down and listened so she wouldn't be mad and she said it looked like what she'd said about the Basic Right hadn't done one bit of good.

Everybody has a right to be different, that was the Basic Right, she said, the foundation of everything and we wouldn't be here now if it weren't for that. And the law says that no one shall discriminate against anyone else because they are different, and that applied to being the same, too. And Miss Harrison said a lot more things I don't remember because I was sort of excited and warm inside. And finally she said she hoped we'd learned a lesson because the Old Race hadn't, and look where they were.

It was right after that I decided I loved Miss Harrison. The other boys say she should have a neck, like Miss Davis, but I don't see why. They say she should have two eyes like me or three like Miss Spencer, but I like her just the way she is and everything she does, like the way she wraps her arm around the chalk when she draws on the board. But I've already said it. I love Miss Harrison.

When I grow up we're going to get married. I've thought of lots of reasons why we should but there's one that's better than any of them.

Miss Harrison and me — I guess we're more different than anybody.

The Homesick Chicken

♦♦♦

BY

EDWARD D.

HOCH

Why did the chicken cross the road?

To get on the other side, you'd probably answer, echoing an old riddle that was popular in the early years of the last century.

But my name is Barnabus Rex, and I have a different answer.

I'd been summoned to the Tangaway Research Farms by the director, an egg-headed old man named Professor Mintor. After parking my car in the guarded lot and passing through the fence — it was an EavesStop, expensive, but sure protection against all kinds of electronic bugging — I was shown into the presence of the director himself. His problem was simple. The solution was more difficult.

"One of the research chickens pecked its way right through the security fence, then crossed an eight-lane belt highway to the other side. We want to know why."

"Chickens are a bit out of my line," I replied.

"But your specialty is the solution of scientific riddles, Mr. Rex, and this certainly is one." He led me out of the main research building to a penned-in area where the test animals were kept. We passed a rein-forced electric cage in which he pointed out the mutated turkeys being bred for life in the domes of the colonies of the moon. Further along were some leggy-looking fowl destined for Mars. "They're particularly well adapted to the Martian terrain and environment," Professor Mintor explained. "We've had to do very little development work; we started from desert roadrunners."

"What about the chickens?"

"The chickens are something else again. The strain, called ZIP-1000, is being developed for breeding purposes on Zipoid, the second planet of Barnard's star. We gave them extra-strength beaks — some-thing like a parrot's — to crack the extra-tough seed hulls used for feed. The seed hulls in turn were developed to withstand the native fauna like the space-lynx and the ostroid, so that —"

"Aren't we getting a little off course?" I asked.

"Ah — yes. The problem. What is a problem is the chicken that crossed the road. It used its extra-strength beak to peck its way right through this security fence. But the puzzling aspect is its motivation. It crossed that belt highway — a dangerous undertaking even for a human — and headed for the field as if it were going home. And yet the chicken was hatched right here within these walls. How could it be homesick for something it had never known?"

"How indeed?" I stared bleakly through the fence at the highway and the deserted field opposite. What was there to attract a chicken — even one of Professor Mintor's super-chickens — to that barren bit of land? "I should have a look at it," I decided. "Can you show me the spot where the chicken crossed the highway?"

He led me around a large pen to a spot in the fence where a steel plate temporarily blocked a jagged hole. I knelt to examine the shards of complex, multiconductor mesh, once more impressed by the securi-ty precautions. "I'd hate to meet your hybrid chickens on a dark night, Professor."

"They would never attack a human being, or even another crea-ture," Mintor quickly assured me. "The beak is used only for cracking seed hulls, and perhaps in self-defense."

"Was it self-defense against the fence?"

He held up his hands. "I can't explain it."

I moved the steel plate and stooped to go through the hole. In that moment I had a chicken's-eye view of the belt highway and the barren field beyond, but they offered no clues. "Be careful crossing over,"

Mintor warned. "Don't get your foot caught!"

Crossing a belt highway on foot — a strictly illegal practice — could be dangerous to humans and animals alike. With eight lanes to traverse it meant hopping over eight separate electric power guides — any one of which could take off a foot if you misstepped. To imagine a chicken with the skill to accomplish it was almost more than I could swallow. But then I'd never before been exposed to Professor Mintor's super-chickens.

The empty lot on the other side of the belt highway held nothing of interest to human or chicken, so far as I could see. It was barren of grass or weeds, and seemed nothing more than a patch of dusty earth dotted with a few pebbles. In a few sunbaked depressions I found the tread of auto tires, hinting that the vacant lot was sometimes used for parking.

I crossed back over the belt highway and reentered the Tangaway compound through the hole in the fence. "Did you find anything?" Mintor asked.

"Not much. Exactly what was the chicken doing when it was recovered?"

"Nothing. Pecking at the ground as if it were back home."

"Could I see it? I gather it's no longer kept outside."

"After the escape we moved them all to the interior pens. There was some talk of notifying Washington since we're under government contract, but I suggested we call you in first. You know how the government is about possible security leaks."

"Is Tangaway the only research farm doing this sort of thing?"

"Oh, no! We have a very lively competitor named Beaverbrook Farms. That's part of the reason for all this security. We just managed to beat them out on the ZIP-1000 contract."

I followed him into a windowless room lit from above by solar panes. The clucking of the chickens grew louder as we passed into the laboratory proper. Here the birds were kept in a large enclosure, constantly monitored by overhead TV. "This one," Mintor said, leading me to a pen that held but a single chicken with its oddly curved beak. It looked no different from the others.

"Are they identified in any way? Laser tattoo, for instance?"

"Not at this stage of development. Naturally when we ship them out for space use they're tattooed."

"I see." I gazed down at the chicken, trying to read something in those hooded eyes. "It was yesterday that it crossed the highway?"

"Yes."

"Did it rain here yesterday?"

"No. We had a thunderstorm two days ago, but it passed over quickly."

"Who first noticed the chicken crossing the road?"

"Granley — one of our gate guards. He was checking security in the parking lot when he spotted it, about halfway across. By the time he called me and we got over there it was all the way to the other side."

"How did you get it back?"

"We had to tranquilize it, but that was no problem."

"I must speak to this guard, Granley."

"Follow me."

The guard was lounging near the gate. I'd noticed him when I arrived and parked my car. "This is Barnabus Rex, the scientific investigator," Mintor announced. "He has some questions for you."

"Sure," Granley replied, straightening up. "Ask away."

"Just one question, really," I said. "Why didn't you mention the car that was parked across the highway yesterday?"

"What car?"

"A parked car that probably pulled away as soon as you started after the chicken."

His eyes widened. "My God, you're right! I'd forgotten it till now! Some kids; it was painted all over stripes, like they're doing these days. But how did you know?"

"Sunbaked tire tracks in the depressions where water would collect. They told me a car had been there since your rain two days ago. Your employees use the lot here, and no visitors would park over there when they had to cross the belt highway to reach you."

"But what does it mean?" Professor Mintor demanded.

"That your mystery is solved," I said. "Let me have a tranquilizer gun and I'll show you."

I took the weapon he handed me and led the way back through the research rooms to the penned-up chickens. Without hesitation I walked up to the lone bird and tranquilized it with a single shot.

"Why did you do that?" Mintor asked.

"To answer your riddle."

"All right. Why *did* the chicken cross the road?"

"Because somebody wanted to play back the contents of a tape recorder implanted in its body. For some time now you've been spied upon, Professor Mintor — I imagine by your competitor, Beaverbrook Farms."

"Spied upon! By that — *chicken?*"

"Exactly. It seemed obvious to me from the first that the fence-pecking chicken was not one of your brood. It was much too strong and much too homesick. But if it wasn't yours it must have been added to your flock surreptitiously, and that could only have been for the purposes of industrial espionage. Since you told me Beaverbrook was doing similar work, this has to be their chicken. I think an X ray will show a micro-miniaturized recorder for listening in on your secret conversations."

"Damnedest thing I ever heard," Professor Mintor muttered, but he issued orders to have the sleeping chicken X-rayed.

"It was a simple task for them to drop the intruding chicken over your fence at night, perhaps lassoing one of your birds and removing it so the count would be right. Those fences are all right for detecting any sort of bugging equipment, but they aren't very good at stopping ordinary intrusion — otherwise that wandering chicken would have set off alarms when it started to cut a hole there. Beaverbrook has been recording your conversations, probably trying to stay one jump ahead on the next government contract. They couldn't use a transmitter in the chicken because of your electronic fence, so they had to recover the bird itself to read out the recording. At the right time, the chicken pecked its way through the fence and started across the highway, but when the guard spotted it the waiting driver panicked and took off. The chicken was left across the road without any way to escape."

"But how did the chicken know when to escape?" asked Mintor. "Could they have some kind of electronic homing device...?"

I smiled, letting the Professor's puzzlement stretch out for a moment. "That was the easiest part," I said at last. "Imprinting."

"But..."

"Exactly. The highly distinctive stripes on the car. The Beaverbrook people evidently trained the chicken from — ah — hatching to associate that pattern with home and food and so on."

A technician trotted up to the professor, waving a photographic negative. "The X rays — there *was* something inside that chicken!"

"Well, Mr. Rex, you were right," the professor conceded.

"Of course, in a sense the chicken *did* cross the road to get to the other side," I admitted. "They always do."

"Have you solved many cases like this one?"

I merely smiled. "Every case is different, but they're always a challenge. I'll send you my bill in the morning — and if you ever need me again, just call."

Technicians

♦♦♦

BY

JEAN

KENWARD

The geometry of sky
      extends its angles. Look,
beyond the hemisphere
     of pen and book
sharp points of light appear
      as if a tall
compass were turning there.
     Stars beyond call
or counting, answer to
      its measurements,
going — man knows not where,
     nor, coming, — whence.

But who can quantify
     the algebra of space,
or weigh those worlds, that swim
      each in its place?
Who can outdo the dark?
     And what computer knows
how beauty comes to birth —
     shell, star and rose?

A Few Things

♦♦♦

BY

MIRIAM
WADDINGTON

There are only a few things
the politicians of war
or the privateers of
free enterprise
haven't yet found out
how to do.

These are to have dreams
and raise children,
be kind and human,
let birds nest
and trees and rivers
live.

Starfish

♦♦♦

ANONYMOUS

As the old man walked down a Spanish beach at dawn, he saw ahead of him what he thought to be a dancer. A young man was running across the sand rhythmically, bending down to pick up a stranded starfish and throw it far into the sea. The old man gazed in wonder as the young man again and again threw the small starfish from the sand to the water. The old man approached him and asked why he spent so much energy doing what seemed a waste of time. The young man explained that the stranded starfish would die if left until the morning sun.

"But there must be thousands of miles of beach and millions of starfish. How can your efforts make any difference?"

The young man looked down at the small starfish in his hand and as he threw it to safety in the sea, said, "It makes a difference to this one."

from

On the Pulse
of Morning

◆◆◆

BY MAYA ANGELOU

Here, root yourselves beside me.
I am that Tree planted by the River,
Which will not be moved.
I, the Rock, I, the River, I, the Tree
I am yours — your passages have been paid.
Lift up your faces, you have a piercing need
For this bright morning dawning for you.
History, despite its wrenching pain,
Cannot be unlived, but if faced
With courage, need not be lived again.

Lift up your eyes
Upon this day breaking for you.
Give birth again
To the dream.

Women, children, men,
Take it into the palms of your hands,
Mold it into the shape of your most
Private need. Sculpt it into
The image of your most public self.
Lift up your hearts
Each new hour holds new chances
For a new beginning.
Do not be wedded forever
To fear, yoked eternally
To brutishness.

The horizon leans forward,
Offering you space
To place new steps of change
Here, on the pulse of this fine day
You may have the courage
To look up and out and upon me,
The Rock, the River, the Tree, your country.
No less to Midas than the mendicant.
No less to you now than the mastodon then.

Here on the pulse of this new day
You may have the grace to look up and out
And into your sister's eyes,
And into your brother's face,
Your country,
And say simply
Very simply
With hope —
Good morning.

ACKNOWLEDGEMENTS

Care has been taken to trace ownership of copyright material contained in this text. The publishers will gladly accept any information that will enable them to rectify any reference or credit in subsequent editions.

TEXT

p. 1 "Metaphors of the Future" by various authors. From *Our Present: Their Future* by Barbara Dixon. Reprinted by permission of OISE Press; **p. 3** "Jason, Becoming" by Gail Fox is reprinted from *Dangerous Season* by permission of Oberon Press; **p. 5** "For My Children" by Robin Mathews. From *Language of Fire: Poems of Love and Struggle* (Toronto: Steel Rail Publishing, 1976). Reprinted by permission; **p. 6** "Hopes and Expectations: How Teenagers View the Future" by Reginald W. Bibby and Donald C. Posterski. From *The Emerging Generation* by Reginald W. Bibby and Donald C. Posterski, pp. 159–167. Toronto: Irwin Publishing. Reprinted by permission of Stoddart Publishing Co. Limited, Don Mills, Ontario; **p. 15** "The Survivor Generation" by various authors. Reprinted by permission of The Canadian Press; **p. 21** "The Girl Who Couldn't See Herself" by Leena Dhingra. From *Right of Way* by The Asian Women Writers' Workshop, first published by The Women's Press Ltd., 1988, 34 Great Sutton Street, London ECIV ODX; **p. 23** "Telephone Romance" by Cathy Beveridge. Reprinted by permission of the author; **p. 29** "Focus on Positive Key to Contentment" by Stephane Wuttunee. Reprinted by permission of the author, Stephane Wuttunee, *Windspeaker* Contributor; **p. 32** "Legacies" by Nikki Giovanni. From *My House* by Nikki Giovanni. Copyright © 1972 by Nikki Giovanni. By permission of William Morrow & Company, Inc.; **p. 33** "If I Had the Wings of an Angel" by Joe Haldeman. Copyright © Joe Haldeman. By permission of the Author and the Author's agent, The Pimlico Agency Inc.; **p. 37** "The Nest" by Robert Zacks. Copyright © 1975 by Robert Zacks. Reprinted by permission of McIntosh & Otis, Inc.; **p. 41** "The Boy, the Balloon, and Open Blue" by Heather Haas Barclay from *The Blue Jean Collection* (Thistledown Press Ltd., 1992), used with permission; **p. 47** "To Open the World" by Karen Connelly was originally published by Reidmore Books in *The Road Home*, 1992; **p. 57** "Learning for Life," excerpts from *Alberta Prospects*. Reprinted with permission of Alberta Advanced Education and Career Development; **p. 62** "Forklift Poem/Winter" by Nick Muska. Reprinted by permission of the author; **p. 65** "Champion of the Deep" by Peggy Orenstein. Copyright © 1991 by The New York Times Company. Reprinted by permission; **p. 74** "A Major Malfunction" by Mike Kilpatrick from *The Blue Jean Collection* (Thistledown Press Ltd., 1992), used with permission; **p. 79** "This Is Just the Beginning" by James Barnes. Reprinted with permission of *Canada and the World* magazine, Oakville, Ontario; **p. 84** "User Friendly" by T. Ernesto Bethancourt copyright © 1989 by T. Ernesto Bethancourt. From *Connections: Short Stories* by Donald B. Gallo, Editor. Used by permission of Delacorte Press, a division of Bantam Doubleday Dell Publishing Group, Inc.; **p. 95** "Machine Mad: Technology isn't always what it's cracked up to be" by Peter Callahan. Reprinted by permission of *Omni*, © 1992, Omni Publications International; **p. 98** "Fantastic Voyages" by D'Arcy Jenish. From *Maclean's* Magazine, Maclean Hunter Ltd., Dec. 14/92; **p. 105** "New Ideas That May Change the Way We Live" by Valérie Anne Giscard d'Estaing and Mark Young. From *Inventions and Discoveries* edited by Valérie Anne Giscard d'Estaing. Copyright © 1993 by Compagnie 2000.

Reprinted with permission by Facts on File, Inc., New York; **p. 109** "More Future Stuff" by Malcolm Abrams and Harriet Bernstein. Excerpts from *More Future Stuff* by Malcolm Abrams and Harriet Bernstein. Copyright © 1991 by Malcolm Abrams and Harriet Bernstein. Illustrations copyright © 1991 by Viking Penguin. Used by permission of Viking Penguin, a division of Penguin Books USA Inc.; **p. 114** "Elephants" by Patrick Lane. From *The Fat Man* by John Newlove. Used by permission of the Canadian Publishers, McClelland & Stewart, Toronto; **p. 117** "Our Mother the Earth Is Growing Old Now" from The Iroquois Confederacy. From *Wisdom of the Elders* by Peter Knudtson and David Suzuki. Reprinted with permission of Stoddart Publishing Co. Limited, Don Mills, Ontario; **p. 126** "Betting On Planet Earth" by John Tierney. Copyright © 1990 by The New York Times Company. Reprinted by permission. Also reprinted by permission from the May 1991 issue of *Reader's Digest*; **p. 133** "What I Did During My Park Vacation" by Ruth Berman. Copyright 1980 by Ruth Berman. From *Microcosmic Tales: 100 Wondrous Science Fiction Short-Short Tales*, ed. Asimov et al, N.Y., Taplinger Company. Reprinted by permission of the author; **p. 135** "The Boy with Five Fingers" by James Gunn. Copyright 1952 by Better Publications Inc. Copyright renewed 1980 by James E. Gunn; **p. 138** "The Homesick Chicken" by Edward D. Hoch. Copyright © 1976 by Edward D. Hoch. First published in Isaac Asimov's *Science Fiction* Magazine. Reprinted by permission of Edward D. Hoch; **p. 143** "Technicians" by Jean Kenward. From *Spaceways*, edited by John Foster, Oxford University Press, 1986. Reprinted by permission of Jean Kenward; **p. 144** "A Few Things" by Miriam Waddington. From *The Last Landscape* by Miriam Waddington. Copyright © by Miriam Waddington 1992. Reprinted by permission of Oxford University Press Canada; **p. 147** "On the Pulse of Morning" by Maya Angelou. Excerpt from *On the Pulse of Morning* by Maya Angelou. Copyright © 1993 by Maya Angelou. Reprinted by permission of Random House, Inc.

PHOTOGRAPHS

p. 4 E. Jane Mundy; **pp. 7, 14** Dick Hemingway; **p. 31** E. Jane Mundy; **p. 49, 53** Ruth Lor Malloy; **p. 56** E. Jane Mundy; **p. 64** Courtesy of Sylvia A. Earle; **p. 73** Elaine Freedman; **p. 83** CAE Industries Ltd.; **p. 97** Reprinted with permission — The Toronto Star Syndicate. Copyright: Tribune Media Services; **p. 101** CAE Industries Ltd.; **p. 103** The Vivid Group; **p. 116** Dick Hemingway; **p. 125** Ruth Lor Malloy; **p. 130** NASA 169-HC-625; **p. 145** Elaine Freedman; **p. 149** Dick Hemingway.